Payment in co

C000135327

A practical guide

**Simon Hughes,   Richard Mills   &
Peter O'Brien**

Acknowledgment

Crown copyright material is reproduced with the permission of the Controller of HMSO and the Queen's Printer for Scotland.

Please note: References to the masculine include, where appropriate, the feminine.

Published by the Royal Institution of Chartered Surveyors (RICS)

Surveyor Court

Westwood Business Park

Coventry CV4 8JE

UK

www.ricsbooks.com

ISBN 978 1 84219 406 5

Typeset in Great Britain by Columns Design Ltd, Reading, Berks

Printed in Great Britain by Page Bros, Milecross Lane, Norwich, NR6 6SA

Table of contents

Table of cases

Payment in construction

1

Introduction

'Cash flow is the lifeblood of the building trade.'

(per Lord Denning in the Court of Appeal in *Dawnays Ltd v FG Minter Ltd and Trollope & Colls Ltd* [1971] 1 WLR 1205)

That such a simple and obvious phrase could result in a huge amount of litigation is evidence of the complex and difficult task of balancing the contractor's need for payment with the employer's need for security by withholding sums where work is not done to a satisfactory standard or within time.

Dawnays case, which limited the employer's right to set-off against payment certificates, was followed in five other Court of Appeal cases before being overturned by the House of Lords in *Modern Engineering (Bristol) Ltd v Gilbert-Ash (Northern) Ltd* [1974] AC 689. This, economic constraints and the absence of an effective dispute resolution tribunal for the construction industry set the tone for two decades of arguments over payment.

In 1993, Sir Michael Latham, who had been appointed by the government to undertake a review of the construction industry, produced his interim report 'Trust and Money'. This report highlighted the then principal failings in the construction industry, namely insufficient trust between the participants in the construction industry which led to late and conditional payments.

In 1994, in his final report 'Constructing the Team', Sir Michael Latham made a number of recommendations, some of which were incorporated into Part II of the *Housing Grants,*

Construction and Regeneration Act 1996 (HGCRA 1996), which came into effect on 1 May 1998, and in the Scheme for Construction Contracts.

Since then there has been a large body of case law seeking to interpret the specific provisions of the Act and the Scheme, with some surprising results.

The government is currently in the process of considering responses to a further review of the Act and the Scheme which is likely to result in some significant changes.

Receiving payment of the correct value and on time is one of the most vital components of a successful enterprise for all participants in the construction process.

This book explains the principles involved and will assist all participants with a greater knowledge of their payment rights, obligations and remedies.

2

Basic payment principles

Introduction

Any consideration of principles governing rights and obligations in relation to payment begins with this: the rights and obligations of the parties regarding payment, just like their other rights and obligations will be governed by the express terms of the contract which they have agreed. However, the law, acting in a sense independent of the will of the parties, will step in under three different scenarios.

Three basic scenarios

There are three basic scenarios which therefore need to be considered:

1 where there is no contract between the parties;
2 where the contract between the parties is silent, or insufficiently detailed, on the question of payment; and
3 in a few specific circumstances, where the law limits the freedom of the parties to agree terms between themselves.

Timing of payments and HGCRA 1996

On top of these three basic scenarios, since the coming into force on 1 May 1998 of the *Housing Grants, Construction and Regeneration Act* 1996 (HGCRA 1996), it is necessary to consider a further very important aspect of payment obligations within construction: the need for a 'construction contract' within the meaning of s. 104 of HGCRA 1996 to provide a payment mechanism which meets the requirements of s. 109 and 110 of HGCRA 1996. This area will be addressed briefly below as although it is not a separate source of payment *obligation* it is relevant to the *timing* of payments.

The existence of the contract

Surprisingly, one of the most frequently encountered issues in practice is the question of whether there is a contract between the parties involved in a project and, if there is, what its terms are. Lots of different variables need to come together, and work, for a construction project to be viable – finance; end-purchasers; builders and suppliers; planning and other regulatory authorities; together with the design for the work. Once these things come together, the pressure to start on site is often extremely great, so that negotiating contractual issues within different parts of the often complex chains of supply is required to be finalised very quickly. At the same time, there can be a desire for each contracting party to remain with its own standard terms of business, or a tension between the requirements of the particular projects and the array of available standard forms, which may not match the particular commercial or other drivers for the project in question.

Construction contracts are often the product of lengthy negotiation over a range of issues such as scope of works, time for completion, specification and performance criteria. In the absence of a written contract it will be a question of importance and often one of some complexity to decide at what point (if at all) in the negotiations the parties reached a concluded agreement. Some important guidelines are expressly set out in *Trollope & Colls Ltd v Atomic Power Constructions Ltd* [1963] 1 WLR 333 and *Pagnan SpA v Feed Products Ltd* [1987] 2 Lloyd's Rep 601 and can be summarised in the following propositions:

- in order to determine whether a contract has been concluded in the course of negotiations, then one must look to the negotiations as a whole;
- there must be an intention by both parties, continuing up to the date of the supposed contract, to make a contract;
- at the date of the supposed contract, the parties must have been of one mind on all the terms which they then regarded as being required in order for that contract to come into existence;
- the terms on which the parties were of one mind does not omit any term which, even though the parties did not realise it, was in fact essential to be agreed, as a term of the contract, if the contract was to be commercially workable;
- in relation to the agreement of further terms, did the parties intend that agreement would not become binding until

there was agreement on further terms, or did the parties intend to be bound forthwith, even though there were terms still to be agreed;

- there must be some manifestation which indicated with sufficient clarity the acceptance by the offeree of the offer as then made to him, such acceptance complying with any stipulation in the offer itself as to the manner of acceptance.

Where the negotiations of the parties are expressed to be 'subject to contract' (or similar words are used to refer to a more formal document being executed at a future time) then there will almost invariably be no concluded contract. Although the factual matrix in which the words are used may be considered, the prima facie effect of the words 'subject to contract' will only be taken away by the most compelling of circumstances.

The existence of standard forms generated by the parties as 'standard terms of business' creates additional complexities in issues of contract formation, especially where each party seeks to impose its terms on the other. The expression 'battle of forms' refers to the situation where there is an offer, followed by a series of counter-offers, all seeking to impose the respective parties' written standard terms of business. The conflict between competing written terms may often be resolved in favour of the party who puts forward the latest terms and conditions; and if they are not objected to by the other party, then he may be taken to have agreed to them. However, it has been said that '[i]n many of these cases our traditional analysis of offer, counter-offer, rejection and acceptance and so forth is out-of-date'. See, for example, Master of the Rolls in *The Butler Machine Tool Company Ltd v Ex-Cell-O Corporation (England) Ltd* [1977] EWCA Civ 9. An analysis based upon simple standards (not rigid rules) of offer and acceptance is almost invariably the correct and practical approach for ascertaining the actual or presumed intentions of the parties to see if they were in agreement.

Some of the more significant counter-decisions are summarised here. In *British Steel Corp v Cleveland Bridge & Engineering Co Ltd* [1984] 1 All ER 504 the plaintiffs (steel fabricators) were approached by the defendants to supply steel-case nodes for incorporating into a building. The plaintiff prepared an estimate for the works based on incomplete information. In February 1979, the defendant gave a letter of intent which: (i) stated the defendant's intention to place a contract with the plaintiff based on prices quoted; (ii) proposed that the contract incorporate the defendant's standard form of subcontract (which provided for unlimited liability on the part of the plaintiff for consequential loss arising out of late delivery); and (iii) required the plaintiff 'to proceed immediately with the works pending the preparation and issuing to you of the official form of sub-contract'. The plaintiff did not reply to the letter of intent. The defendant then indicated that it required delivery of the nodes in a particular sequence, and there followed further discussions after which the specification was subsequently changed. The plaintiff proceeded to manufacture and deliver the nodes, although the parties were unable to agree on progress payments and liability for loss due to late delivery. By December 1979, all but one of the nodes had been delivered. The defendant refused to make any interim payment for the nodes delivered, and instead sent a claim to the plaintiff for damages for late delivery. The plaintiff issued proceedings, contending that no contract had been made between the parties, and claiming the value of the nodes. Robert Goff J held that there was no contract, and said:

'In the present case, an unresolved dispute broke out between the parties on the question of whether CBE's or BSC's standard terms were to apply, the former providing no limit to the seller's liability or delay and the latter excluding such liability altogether. Accordingly, when in a case such as the present, the parties are still in a state of negotiations, it is impossible to predicate what liability (if any) will be assumed by the seller for, e.g. defective goods or late delivery, if a formal contract should be entered into. In these circumstances, if the buyer asks the seller to commence work "pending" the parties entering into a formal contract, it is difficult to infer from the buyer acting on that request that he is assuming any responsibility for his performance, except such responsibility as will rest on him under the terms of the contract which both parties confidently anticipate they will shortly enter into.'

In *Drake & Scull Engineering Ltd v Higgs & Hill Northern Ltd* (1995) 11 Const LJ 214 the defendants were main contractors for certain works to a Liverpool hospital, and they invited the plaintiffs to tender for the supply and installation of mechanical and electrical installations. There was extensive correspondence between the parties in relation to design obligations, the plaintiffs' daywork rates, and whether formal contract documentation would be entered into. The Official

Referee found that all matters of dispute were resolved by May 1991, save for the fixing of the plaintiffs' daywork rates, which both parties regarded as essential. No further relevant correspondence passed until May 1993. The plaintiffs commenced work in April 1992 and completed in July 1993. The Official Referee, finding a contract between the parties, said:

> 'I am satisfied that, by May 11, all the terms save one necessary for a binding contract to come into being were "agreed". That is to say, inter alia, price, commencement date of the contract, duration of the contract and obligations under the contract. The fact that D&S had no design obligation save for the extremely limited development of design requirements was only reached on May 11, but it was resolved on that date. The only matter which was not agreed at that time were the daywork rates. It is clear that up to May 12, both parties were regarding agreement on daywork rates as an essential matter. The potential importance of reaching agreement may be gauged from the fact that in the absence of agreement D&S have as yet been unable to recover any payment for the daywork that they have done. But I have reached the conclusion on the basis of the arguments advanced by Mr. Collins QC that if the failure to agree daywork rates was the only matter which might have prevented the coming into being of a contract, that lacuna would be made good by the implication of a term that D&S should be paid a reasonable sum.'

In *Mitsui Babcock Energy Ltd v John Brown Engineering Ltd* (1996) 51 Con LR 129 the defendants were the main contractors for the construction of a 600 MW combined cycle power station. They engaged the plaintiffs to design, manufacture and install two generators. In May 1992, the defendants issued a letter of intent to the plaintiffs, followed by negotiations over performance tests which were provided for in Clause 35 of the standard form MF1. The defendants pressed for strict compliance with the design requirements and for payment of substantial sums as liquidated damages if the generators failed to pass the performance tests. In the result, Clause 35 was struck out and a marginal annotation 'to be discussed and agreed' was inserted. The contract documents were signed on behalf of both parties in June 1993. In September 1995, the defendants sent a letter to the plaintiffs alleging that there was no contract. The Official Referee holding that there was a contract, said that 'the parties made a coherent and workable contract' which was not invalidated by the failure to arrive at an agreement on Clause 35. The Official Referee also observed that the parties operated the contract provisions up to September 1995.

Frequently asked questions

Q. What is the contractual position if a party was issued with a 'letter of intent', worked on the basis of the letter, and no formal contract of the kind anticipated in the letter of intent ever materialised?

A. It depends on the terms of the letter of intent. If the letter of intent is marked as 'subject to contract', or if similar words to that effect are used, then no contract will have come into existence. However, if the letter of intent is sufficiently detailed and is not marked 'subject to contract' then a contract based on the terms of the letter of intent may well have come into existence.

Q. Section 107 of HGCRA 1996 says that adjudication only applies to contracts in writing. What does this mean in practice?

A. The Act will only apply if all of the terms of the contract are in writing. If some of the terms are agreed orally or are implied by conduct then the Act will not apply. See Ward LJ in *RJT Consulting Engineers Ltd v DM Engineering (NI) Ltd* [2002] BLR 217.

Q. What approach will the courts take where there is no clear 'offer' and no clear 'acceptance' but there has been full performance on the basis that the contract was on a particular basis?

A. The courts will look at all the documents passing between the parties and the conduct of the parties to establish whether the parties have reached agreement on all material points. If the court concludes that the parties have reached such a conclusion then a contract will be in place based on that agreement.

Quantum meruit

Where there is no contract between the parties, the contractor carrying out work at the request of the employer, or the subcontractor for the main contractor, will be entitled to be paid a *quantum meruit* for what he has done.

Some of the basic principles are summarised below:

1   A *quantum meruit* is a fair commercial rate for the work done.
2   Generally speaking, the focus of the valuation exercise is on the work provided by the contractor rather than upon the value of the work to the recipient of the work (or services). Hence, a builder who carries out significant preparatory work for a project that is then not proceeded with by his employer is entitled to be paid a fair commercial rate for the work done even though it did not lead to a tangible benefit to his employer. However, benefits conferred on the employer by the work of the contractor can be taken into account in the valuation of the fair commercial rate (*Zanen* case).
3   In coming to a fair commercial rate for work done, the correct approach is to look at the value of the work in the marketplace (*Greenmast Shipping* case), but then taking into account all the circumstances.
4   Where a contract was negotiated but not ultimately entered into, the rates and prices in the abortive contract can be relevant to fair commercial rate (*Way v Latilla*).
5   In practice, the question arises as to the factors that the court will consider in arriving at a fair commercial rate for the work done. Each case will be looked at on its individual facts and circumstances, and the court will look at all the surrounding circumstances. Whatever else is used, it is usually helpful to establish actual costs incurred for the work. Standard industry rates, or pricing books, can play a role, provided the overall context and circumstances of the work is not forgotten (*Floods* and the *Lachhani* cases).
6   Valuation of a *quantum meruit* is an area where it is useful to look at the approach taken by the courts in the decided cases, and some of the most important cases are summarised below.

Way v Latilla [1937] 3 All ER 759 (HL)

In the decision of *Latilla* the appellant entered into an agreement with the respondent for the provision of information relating to gold mines and concessions in West Africa. It was also agreed the respondent would provide the appellant with shares in the concessions and pay a reasonable sum for the information. The respondent failed to provide the appellant with the shares, as agreed or at all.

The House of Lords decided that the appropriate method for arriving at a reasonable sum was to pay regard to previous conversations and participation of the parties. Lord Atkin stated:

> 'The question of the amount to which the appellant is entitled is left at large, and the court must do the best it can to arrive at a figure which seems to it fair and reasonable to both parties.'

Greenmast Shipping Co SA v Jean Lion CIE SA [1986] 2 Lloyd's Rep 277

In the decision of *Greenmast Shipping Co* the facts were that a vessel was hired by its owners to charterers for the carriage of a cargo. At the request of the charterers the vessel waited nine days to enable the charterers to resolve a problem. It was common ground that the owner was entitled to reasonable remuneration for acceding to the request.

The Court decided that the appropriate method for arriving at a reasonable sum was to award the owners a 'fair commercial rate' (Mr Justice Saville).

Batis Maritime Corporation v Petroleos del Mediterraneo SA [1990] 1 Lloyd's Rep 345

In the decision of *Batis* the facts were that the owners let their vessel *Batis* to the charterers for a voyage. There were specific terms in the charter as to the cargo and the nomination of ports by the charterers. Arbitrators found that the charterers had breached the charter.

The Court held that on the basis that the charterers breached the charter the owners were entitled to recover on the basis of *quantum meruit*. It held that in assessing the sum due the

Court must have regard to: all the expenses incurred by the owners in rendering those services; and the whole amount of the expenses incurred by way of additional war risks premium. The extra war premiums were only incurred as a result of the charterer's breach (Mr Justice Hobhouse: case applied *Greenmast*).

Laserbore Ltd v Morrison Biggs Wall Ltd (1993) CILL

In the decision of *Laserbore Ltd* the facts were that the claimants claimed payment for microtunnelling done by them as subcontractors to the defendants who were acting as main contractors for Shell. The defendants also made a small counter-claim. The defendants withheld payment on the basis that the works were unsatisfactory.

The Court decided that the appropriate method for arriving at a reasonable sum was to award the claimants a 'fair commercial rate for the services provided'.

Sanjay Lachhani v Destination Canada (UK) Ltd (1996) 13 Const LJ 279

In the decision in *Sanjay Lachhani* the facts were that the defendants required building works to be carried out. The defendant approached Mr Vaghjiani for the main contract works. He approached the claimants and led them to believe he was an authorised representative of the defendant. Both the defendants and claimants believed there to be a contract in place for the works to be completed by 'x' date at 'x' price. In fact, no contract existed. The claimants failed to complete the works by 'x' date.

The Court decided that the appropriate method for arriving at a 'fair value' ought to 'recognise an entitlement to a reasonable or normal profit margin over and above the costs actually and properly incurred in carrying out the work'. Mr Recorder Reese QC also held that the fair value will vary on a case-by-case basis.

Serck Controls Ltd v Drake & Scull Engineering Ltd [2000] All ER (D) 725

In the decision of *Serck* the facts were that the claimants carried out work for the defendants. No contract existed. A letter of intent from the defendants to the claimants provided that in the event that the parties were unable to agree satisfactory terms and conditions in respect of the overall package, the defendants 'would undertake to reimburse [the claimants] with all reasonable costs incurred'.

The Court held that the sum due was to be 'assessed by reference to what would have been reasonable remuneration for executing work, rather than its value to D [the defendants]'.

ACT Construction v Clarke & Sons [2002] EWCA Civ 972

In the decision of *ACT* the facts were that the claimant carried out works for the defendant. There was no formal contract. The claimant made a number of interim applications for payment, for which only one payment was made in full. The defendant was in financial difficulty and asked the claimant to leave. The claimant left and discontinued the work.

The Court of Appeal held that a contract did exist but with no agreed terms as to price. It was therefore implied that the claimant would receive a reasonable sum. This sum was assessed at costs plus 15 per cent on all works completed.

Robertson Group v Amey-Miller (Edinburgh) Joint Venture [2005] CSOH 60 (Scottish case)

In the decision of *Robertson* the facts were that the claimant and defendant entered into a temporary contract for refurbishment work. The terms were set out in a letter that stated: 'Should a formal contract fail to be entered into, then all direct costs and directly incurred losses shall be underwritten and reimbursed by the Joint Venture.' Works were carried out. Disputes ensued between the parties and as a result no formal contract could be made.

Lord Drummond Young in the Inner House Court of Session held that 'all direct costs and directly incurred losses' entitled the claimant to 'recover reasonable sums by way of general corporate overheads and profits'.

Costain Civil Engineering Ltd v Zanen Dredging [1996] 85 BLR 77

In the decision of *Zanen* the facts were that instructions containing variations were purported to be given under a subcontract. The arbitrator found that the variations were outside the scope of the contract and therefore payment to *Zanen* was to be on the basis of *quantum meruit*.

The Queen's Bench Division (QBD) held that the arbitrator's decision that a reasonable sum be assessed on the basis of costs and profits was correct (His Honour Judge D Wilcox; p. 83 sets out how to calculate costs and profits).

ERDC Group Ltd v Brunel University [2006] BLR 255 (TCC)

In the decision of *ERDC* the facts were that the claimant carried out works for the defendant on the basis of a JCT Standard Form Contract with Contractor's Design, 1998 edition. Pending planning permission, the claimant commenced works under various letters of intention. Upon the expiry of the final letter, the claimant continued to work only on the basis that the work would be valued on a *quantum meruit* basis.

The Technology and Construction Court (TCC) held that works carried out under the letters of appointment were valued by applying relevant 'rates and prices'. The relationship had moved from a contractual to a non-contractual basis and in these unusual circumstances it was also appropriate to apply the 'rates and prices' method.

Frequently asked questions

Q. Are there significant tactical advantages to arguing 'no contract' such as the ability to move from contract rates and prices to some form of 'costs plus' remuneration?

A. In a 'no contract' scenario actual costs will be important but so will previously agreed rates and prices. 'No contract' does not always mean 'costs plus'. Of course there may also be other consequences such as Part II of HGCRA 1996 not applying and the huge uncertainty that will exist over other rights and obligations such as termination, specification and liability for defects.

Q. How does the court deal with defective work where there is no contract and the contractor is to be paid on a *quantum meruit* basis?

A. When valuing work on a *quantum meruit* basis the court will usually value the work as if it had been properly done and then deduct the cost of rectifying any defective work or if the cost of rectification is disproportionate to the benefit to be gained, make an allowance for loss of amenity.

Q. Accepting that the courts can look at 'all the circumstances' in deciding how to value a reasonable sum, is the reality that in most cases the contractor will be entitled to remuneration based essentially on cost?

A. In most cases cost will be an important factor in determining a fair value but this does not mean that the courts will ignore previously agreed rates and prices or market conditions.

Payment governed by express terms

It is a basic point, but always emphasised by the courts, that parties should read their contracts because the courts will generally do no more than give effect to the express words which have been agreed. A number of general guiding principles are worth noting.

Basic rules of interpretation of contracts apply. The most important guide in principle is that the court or an arbitrator will seek to give effect to the ordinary (or, where appropriate, accepted) meaning of the words used by the parties in their contract, based upon the use of a series of rules or 'canons' of construction. These are summarised briefly below.

1   *Ordinary meaning:* The court adopts the ordinary meaning of an ordinary English word, unless it is contended that the word has an alternative meaning in the context. The ordinary meaning of the word is to be considered in light of the contract as a whole. *Harbinger UK Ltd v GE Information Services Ltd* [2001] 1 All ER (Comm) 166, [2000] 2 TCLR 463, CA.

2   *Reasonable meaning:* The court will apply an objective business common-sense approach when interpreting ambiguous terms of a commercial contract. *Antaios Compania Naviera SA v Salen Rederierna AB* [1985] AC

191, HL; *Sirius International Insurance Co (Publ) v FAI General Insurance Ltd and others* [2004] All ER (D) 24 (Dec), [2004] UKHL 54; *City & General (Holborn) Ltd v AYH plc* [2006] BLR 55 (TCC).

3   *Contract to be read as a whole:* The contract must be construed as a whole, giving effect to each of the provisions where practicable. The court therefore determines which documents are contractual and then gives effect to each of the provisions in the contractual document. *Brodie v Cardiff Corp* [1919] AC 337 at 355, HL ; *Aqua Design v Kier Regional Ltd* [2003] BLR 111.

4   *Term of art:* This is a word or phrase that has a precise legal meaning when it is ordinarily applied by the courts. The word or phrase may, however, not be a term of art if included in a document by an author who is not a lawyer who did not anticipate that the document would be construed by a lawyer. *LCC v Boot (Henry) & Sons Ltd* [1959] 1 WLR 1069 at 1075, HL.

5   *Internal consistency:* The same words used in a document will be presumed to have the same meaning throughout the entirety of the document. Different words will refer to different things. *John Jarvis v Rockdale Housing Association* [1986] 38 BLR 48 at 61, CA.

6   *Contra proferentem rule:* Where there is an ambiguity in a document that cannot be resolved and there are two alternative meanings to a certain word and/or phrase, the court may construe the word and/or phrase against the party that drafted or tendered the document. *John Lee & Sons v Railway Executive* [1949] 2 All ER 581 at 583, CA.

7   *Extrinsic evidence is not normally admissible:* Generally, in a written contract, no evidence outside the document itself can be adduced to contradict, vary, add to or subtract from the written terms. *National Westminster Bank v Halesowen Presswork* [1972] AC 785 at 818, HL; *Proforce Recruit Ltd v The Rugby Group Ltd* [2006] All ER (D) 247 (Feb).

8   *Preliminary negotiations:* Once parties have entered into a final concluded contract in writing, the parties cannot, save in limited circumstances, rely on pre-contractual negotiations and documents for the purpose of explaining the parties' intention. *Kinlen v Ennis UDC* [1916] 2 IR 299, CA.

9   *Subsequent conduct:* Once the contract has been made the parties cannot rely on subsequent conduct to explain the construction of the contract (*Whitworth Street Estates (Manchester) Ltd v James Miller & Partners Ltd* [1970] AC 583 at 603, HL; *Maggs v Marsh* [2006] EWCA Civ 1058,

CA), even where ambiguity exists. *Schuler AG v Wickman Machine Tool Sales Ltd* [1974] AC 235 at 252.

10 *Factual background:* Restricted evidence is admissible to ascertain the factual background known to the parties at or before the date of the contract. *Prenn v Simmonds* [1971] 1 WLR 1381 at 1385, *Nearfield Ltd v Lincoln Nominees Ltd & another* [2006] All ER (d) 93 (Oct); [2006] EWHC 2421 (ch).

11 *Surrounding circumstances:* Save for pre-contractual negotiations the court can consider factors other than the words in the contractual document to ascertain the contractual intentions of the parties. *Prenn v Simmonds* [1971] 1 WLR 1381 at 1385, HL; *Proforce Recruit Ltd v The Rugby Group Ltd* [2006] All ER (D) 247 (Feb).

For these reasons, and in most situations, the court will rely on an ordinary meaning of the words used by the parties. Thus, it is extremely important that careful attention is paid to the words used, or the standard form which this incorporated. Although the court will strive, so far as possible, to uphold what it regards as the clear commercial intention of the parties, care nevertheless needs to be taken, for example, in the situation where the 'main contract' terms are thought to be imported wholesale into a 'subcontract'. Where no appropriate amendments are made in this case, then certainly the court will strive to give effect to the incorporation by reference, but the parties need to be aware that there may be great practical difficulties in 'reading down' main contract terms into a subcontract. Parties should also be very cautious before assuming that words and phrases used in their building contract have an accepted meaning which does not need to be explained or fully worked through in the particular contract documentation. For example, from a common-sense point of view, it may appear obvious that 'provisional sums' fall to be deducted from the contract sum once actual costs for the work have been identified. However, it is still necessary for the parties, in their contract, to spell out the precise mechanism whereby sums are to be added, and other sums are to be omitted, in the context of provisional sums.

In a number of specified scenarios, the courts will require clear words in the parties' contract before reaching the conclusion that certain rights or remedies have been excluded by the contract made by the parties. A very good example is the right of set-off.

Some contractual provisions seek to prevent parties from relying upon what would otherwise be their legal rights at common law. In general, parties are permitted to do so but in *Gilbert-Ash (Northern) v Modern Engineering (Bristol) Ltd* [1974] AC 689 at 717 Lord Diplock stated in relation to an alleged risk to exclude a right of set-off against payments under a building contract:

> 'In construing such a contract one starts with the presumption that neither party intends to abandon any remedies for its breach arising by operation of law, and clear express words must be used in order to rebut this presumption.'

In most cases, a right of set-off will only be excluded where the clause refers to set-off expressly.

A similar principle applies where the contract seeks to restrict one party's right to adduce evidence in relation to a dispute which would be admissible were that dispute to be litigated in court, for example, where it seeks to prevent one party from relying on a non-compliant sample in support of a claim to reject goods. The same approach is also applied where it is alleged that a contract deprives an injured contracting party of damages to which he would otherwise be entitled.

Where a clause in a contract does exclude a remedy, the clause will be narrowly construed. Thus, in *Acsim (Southern) Ltd v Danish Contracting and Development Co Ltd* [1992] 47 BLR 59, a building contract provided that the rights of the parties as to set-off were fully set out in the contract and no other rights relating to set-off should be implied. The Court of Appeal held that the reference to 'set-off' was to be construed as a reference to set-off as defined by judicial decisions, and did not prevent the employer from defending itself against a claim for payment on the ground that the value of the work for which the sum was claimed had been diminished by the contractor's breaches of contract (abatement).

Payment governed by implied terms (no agreed price)

Where there is no agreed price in the contract between the parties, the courts will readily imply a term that the provider of the work or services is to be paid a reasonable sum. The *Supply of Goods and Services Act* 1982 (SOGSA 1982) (Part II) is applicable to contracts for the supply of goods and services, and this includes construction contracts. Subject to the possibility of exclusion or restriction in accordance with s. 16, a supplier of a service acting in the course of business is obliged to carry out the service with reasonable skill and care; there will be an implied term that the supplier will carry out the service within a reasonable time; and there will be an implied term that the party contracting with the supplier will pay the supplier a reasonable charge. Section 16 provides that the obligation created by SOGSA 1982 may be negatived or varied by express agreement, by the course of dealing between the parties, or by such usage as binds both parties to the contract, but a term implied by SOGSA 1982 is not negatived by an express term of the contract between the parties unless it is inconsistent with it.

Section 15 of SOGSA 1982 provides that the party contracting with the supplier will pay the supplier a reasonable charge. Section 2 of SOGSA 1982 provides that a reasonable charge will be a question of fact for the court to decide. It is submitted that the broad range of considerations open to the court on a *quantum meruit* will be used in this context, also.

Frequently asked questions

Q. What can the court do if the interpretation of the contract reached by simply looking at the ordinary meaning of the words is manifestly unfair and uncommercial?

A. If the words are clear and there is no evidence of fraud or misrepresentation or duress then the court will usually apply the clear meaning of the words. See, for example, *Henry Boot Construction v Alstom Combined Cycles Ltd* [2000] BLR 247, CA. If there is ambiguity in the words and the court is faced with two or more possible interpretations then the court will tend to prefer the interpretation which supports the objective business common-sense approach.

In contracts with consumers or contracts made on the written standard terms of business of one of the parties the court may also have recourse to the *Unfair Contract Terms Act* 1977, as amended, which subjects exclusion clauses to a test of reasonableness.

Q. What is rectification of a contract, and how does it differ from rules in relation to the interpretation of the contract?

A. Rectification is where the court is satisfied that the written contract does not reflect the actual agreement made by the parties. In these circumstances the court has power to change the written contract to reflect the actual agreement. Rectification is very rare and convincing proof of the common mistake is required. It will usually be in one of the parties' interests to argue that it intended to enter into the contract as drafted.

Q. Frequently, in contracts such as the NEC, parties include as part of the contract documents a schedule of correspondence, including correspondence in relation to pre-contractual negotiations. How is this to be treated?

A. These are sometimes referred to as numbered documents and are incorporated into the contract by reference. Often the contract will have a 'priorities of documents' clause which will set out how these documents are to be treated. In such a case the court will follow the rules set out in that clause. In the absence of such a clause the court will interpret the contract as a whole giving equal weight to all of the documents including those incorporated by reference. In the event of ambiguity or inconsistency and in the absence of a clause setting out how such ambiguity or inconsistency is to be resolved the court will apply the rules of interpretation set out above.

Time for payment under HGCRA 1996

Since 1 May 1998, and the coming into force of HGCRA 1996, no discussion of basic payment mechanisms in construction would be complete without reference to the compulsory payment regime instituted by HGCRA 1996. A full discussion of the regime is covered in detail in Chapter 8.

3

Types of contract

On the question of payment, when the parties set about looking for appropriate terms and conditions, they will need to think of the express terms of the contract as a set of rules to be followed, like an instruction manual, and the more successful contracts will select, or provide for, an instruction manual which best suits the project, the way in which the work is to be procured and carried out, and the position of the two parties. In the construction and engineering fields, there is an array of standard forms available, with elements of 'bolt-on' extras, and the parties can then either alter that standard form documentation or use their own standard terms or prepare their own job-specific terms and conditions. Most problems arise where the terms and conditions of payment which are used simply do not 'fit' with the project, the way in which the work is to be procured and carried out, and the position of the two parties.

Key components of the contract

Some key components will be explained and explored:

1   schedule of work;
2   bill of quantities;
3   schedules of cost components (NEC);
4   schedule of rates; and
5   contract sum analysis.

Schedule(s) of work

A schedule of work can be as basic as a list of items of work to be completed, with no or little description and no quantities. A schedule in this format might simply say 'Wall' or 'Build Wall'.

Usually, the schedule of work will be more detailed, or else there will be a separate document which sets out the standard or quality of workmanship to be achieved (often called the specification). This itself will be supplemented by standards or industry documents which are referenced in the specification, and there will usually be sketches or drawings for the works which identify location, dimensions and the relationship between the elements to be built or provided.

Example output specification for a new school

1.0	Design and Construction Requirements
1.2.5.2	Science
1.2.5.2.1	Activities that need to be accommodated included small groups of students carrying out experiments, or individual students working on their own. Teacher demonstrations will take place, and the siting of the teacher's position should allow students to see clearly what the teacher is doing.
1.2.5.2.2	The science laboratories should be grouped together on one floor, to enable the maximising of resources.
1.2.5.2.3	The preparation spaces shall be located centrally to the laboratories to avoid the unnecessary movement of material.
1.2.5.2.4	Each laboratory shall accommodate 30 pupils including one wheelchair user. This will require an element of variable-height science benching.
1.2.5.3	Art
1.2.5.3.1	A general art space can cover a broad range of activities, including textiles or ceramics, which will require larger spaces than an art space used only for drawing and painting. Spaces will be used to provide 3D and 2D art studios. Reference should be made to Building Bulletin 89, 'Art Accommodation in Secondary Schools' and 'A Guide to Safe Practice in Art and Design'.
1.2.5.3.2	The art spaces shall be located within easy access of design areas.
1.2.5.3.3	Art spaces shall have good quality natural lighting especially for activities such as drawing and painting. The rooms should ideally be north facing to attract the most benefit from natural light.
1.2.5.3.4	Group sizes will vary but the rooms need to accommodate up to 30 pupils including provision for one wheelchair user.

Bill of quantities

The status and use of bills of quantities vary significantly between the various standard form contracts, and it will be a question in each individual case quite what status the bill of quantities has. This will depend in part upon the nature of the detail to be found in the bill of quantities which the parties use, but also upon the terms of the contract as a whole. Where the bill of quantities is a full contract document (as under the ICE conditions of contract), then any general provisions incorporated into the bill will have full contractual effect, and will need to be read together with the rest of the contract documents. By way of comparison, under the JCT Form of Building Contract, the bill is generally regarded as having a more limited status in terms of defining quality and quantity of the work, and will often be regarded as not overriding or modifying the conditions of contract. See, for example, Clause 1.3 in JCT SBC 05 with Quantities. In such a case, any provision within the bill purporting to modify the conditions – for example, provision for sectional completion – may be construed as having no effect despite the apparent intention of the parties (*Gleeson v London Borough of Hillingdon* (1970) 215 *Estates Gazette* 165). Once again, the effect of the bills of quantities will depend upon whether the contract provides for a remeasure of the work and/or whether the conditions provide for a correction of the bill in the event of departures from the standard method of measurement.

Example bill of quantities for a railway bridge

Item	Description	Qty	Unit	Rate	£ p
	STRUCTURAL CONCRETE				
	In Situ Concrete				
A	In situ concrete mix reference D23/24/1 in deck	145	m³	96.45	13,985.25
B	In situ concrete mix reference D23/24/1 in parapet edge beams	24	m³	98.99	2,375.76
	Surface Finish of Concrete-Formwork				
C	Formwork Class F2 horizontal more than 300 mm wide to parapet edge beams and oversail soffits	85	m²	64.67	5,496.95

D	Permanent formwork EMJ Type 8 horizontal more than 300 mm wide to deck	546	m²	82.68	45,143.28
E	Curved formwork Class F2 of both girth and width more than 300 mm at any inclination to parapet edge beams	32	m²	67.56	2,161.92
F	Curved formwork Class F2 of girth of width 300 mm or less at any inclination to parapet edge beams	26	m²	69.43	1,805.18

Schedules of cost components (NEC)

The schedule of cost components (and the shorter schedule of cost components) are particular features of certain standard forms within the NEC suite of contracts, now in their third edition (referred to either as 'NEC 3' or 'ECC 3rd edition'). The full version of the schedule only applies when option C, D or E is used. By virtue of the definition of defined cost (which used to be called 'actual cost' under NEC 2) under Clause 11.2(22), the contracts used within options A and B use the shorter schedule. The central purpose of the schedules is to identify those components of expenditure which will be allowable with the pricing of compensation events. Under different headings (people, equipment, plant and materials, design, etc.) the type of reasonable expenditure is identified and the overall method of its calculation is explained.

Schedule of rates

Where the design of the works is not sufficiently developed for a bill of quantities to be put together, then a contract may be based upon a schedule of rates. No quantities are provided, but rates and prices for particular elements of work are identified, so that the schedule can be used to measure entitlement, either as the work proceeds or at the end, when the scope of the work is clearer. The tenderer is usually either invited to provide a percentage adjustment to rates included by the employer (or his representative) or else provide rates and prices of his own as part of his tender bid.

Contract sum analysis

In the JCT Design and Build Form, generally speaking, the means by which the contractor proposes to satisfy the requirements contained in the employer's requirements, will be set out and described in the contractor's proposals. This document will identify the basis for the design and construction of the works and will include drawings and a specification. The contractor's contract sum analysis will be less detailed and often less prescriptive than the bill of quantities typically used within JCT contracts with quantities. The purpose of the contract sum analysis is to provide an overall indication to the employer of the way in which the contractor's price has been developed, although it also provides the basis upon which additional, substituted or omitted work is valued and the basis upon which interim payments may be calculated.

Frequently asked questions

Q. What are the principal purposes of pricing documents?

A. Historically, bills of quantities were prepared by tendering contractors to enable them to price the works. Several tenderers would often get together to jointly commission preparation of the bills so as to save tendering costs. In order to avoid the obvious opportunity for collusion that this arrangement created clients began to take responsibility for preparing the bills and issuing them to the contractors with the tender documents. This reduced the opportunity for collusion between tenderers, reduced the time required to prepare tenders, improved communications between bill producers and designers, provided surveyors with valuable costing information for use when estimating future projects and provided surveyors with costing information to assist with the valuation of variations and interim payments.

Q. Will pricing documents always be used to price variations?

A. Pricing variations is usually one of the principal purposes for requesting priced documents but not exclusively. Often contract sum analyses are insufficiently detailed to offer any useful assistance in pricing variations. Also the NEC form requires additional works to be priced using defined cost (actual cost) unless the project manager and contractor agree otherwise.

Pricing strategies

Some key pricing strategies will be explained and explored:

1 lump sum contract;
2 measure and value;
3 guaranteed maximum price; and
4 incentivised contracts: gain/pain sharing and value engineering.
5 target costs contracts;
6 prime cost contract;
7 contracts with and without quantities/contracts with approximate quantities; and
8 costs plus a fee (see JCT management contract).

In one sense, there are as many pricing strategies for construction contracts as there are construction contracts themselves, and each contract needs to be carefully interpreted in accordance with all of its express terms, and not by simply assuming that frequently used terms have a fixed status and meaning in every case. In this sense, as mentioned elsewhere, it is absolutely essential for the parties to remember that building contracts are to be construed in accordance with the very same principles as applied to commercial contracts generally. However, some of the most prominent pricing strategies used within the UK and overseas building industries are discussed briefly below.

Lump sum contracts

In a lump sum contract, the builder is required to carry out and complete the entirety of precisely identified contract works for a fixed sum agreed in advance. If there are changes in the scope of the identified contract works, then the lump sum is adjusted and becomes payable in the manner specified in the contract conditions. Generally speaking, where there is a lump sum contract, then the proposed contract works will be of known extent – which is to say, rarely at the early design or development stage – and will typically be described in some detail in the specification, bills of quantities or in drawings or, more usually, a combination of these. Where the work in the lump sum contract is sufficiently described – and there are no particular formalities required as to the manner of description – then a court or arbitrator is likely to conclude that, in exchange for being paid the lump sum, the builder has agreed to carry out and complete all of the work described, or reasonably to be inferred from, the language and/or descriptions in the contract documents. The problems frequently arise where the description provided by the contract documents is vague or inadequate. This will be a question of fact and degree in the individual case. However, where work is not sufficiently described, and the necessity to carry out the work cannot reasonably be inferred from the language or descriptions to be found in the contract documents, then the builder will be entitled to be paid sums in addition to the lump sum price in respect of the work required to be carried out but not described in the contract documents (see *Bryant & Sons v Birmingham Hospital Saturday Fund* (1988) 9 Con LR 128).

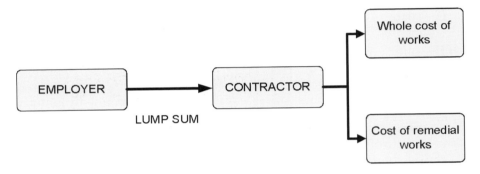

Examples

- NEC 3rd edition, Professional Services Contract: *Option A: A priced contract*
- JCT 2005, IC: *Intermediate Building Contract*
- JCT 2005, ICD: *Intermediate Building Contract with Contractor's Design*
- JCT 2005, MW: *Minor Works Building Contract*
- JCT 2005, DB: *Design and Build Contract*
- JCT 2005, SHORTSUB: *Short Form of Sub-Contract*

Measure and value/remeasurement contracts

Work carried out under a remeasurement contract is measured and valued, typically as the work proceeds, so that there is no need for a pre-agreed lump sum. Valuations are normally made by the project engineer (ICE, FIDIC) or the architect (JCT with provisional quantities). Typically, the contract includes a bill of quantities in which the quantities are estimated, and rates are inserted with the intention that they should form the basis for the remeasurement of work carried out. In such a case, it is usual for the parties to agree a mechanism whereby the agreed rates and prices to be found in the provisional bill of quantities is linked to anticipated quantities of work, so that large increases and decreases in quantity of work (upon a remeasurement) can give rise to a revaluation of the rates and prices.

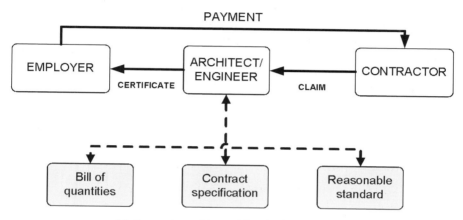

Matters relevant to architect's determination

Examples

- NEC 3rd edition, Professional Services Contract: *Option E: Time based contract*
- NEC 3rd edition, Engineering and Construction Subcontract: *Option B: Priced subcontract with bill of quantities*
- NEC 3rd edition, Engineering and Construction Contract: *Option B: Priced subcontract with bill of quantities*
- JCT 2005, SBQ/AQ: *Standard Building Contract with Approximate Quantities*
- ICE conditions, 7th edition: *Measurement Version*

Guaranteed maximum price

Caution needs to be exercised with the phrase 'guaranteed maximum price' (GMP). It will be a question of construction in each case whether, by their contract, the parties have bound themselves to a price which is not, without further agreement, capable of adjustment. It is submitted that very clear words would be required to create a GMP or fixed price in circumstances where, for example, the contract made it clear that the scope of the works was uncertain or certainly not fixed.

See, for example, the opinion of Lord Drummond Young in the case of *City Inn Ltd v Shepherd Construction Ltd* [2007] Outer House, Court of Session.

Incentivised contracts

Increasingly, within the construction industry, contracting parties wish to make arrangements to both incentivise the attainment of project targets and also to distribute the risk of non-performance, or under-performance, between the parties on the project. These types of arrangements have a number of different distinct features. It is often the case that the parties, at the design and development stage, institute a process of value engineering aimed at incentivising the attainment of best design/best prices for key components of the works. The acceptance of value engineering proposals, and the savings derived from this process, are commonly divided in agreed proportions between the contracting parties. At later stages in the project, it is often the case that pain share/gain share arrangements will seek to arrive at a division of 'gains' or 'losses' (pain) derived from agreed target prices or deliverables.

Examples

- NEC 3rd edition, ECC (bonus for early completion)
- NEC 3rd edition, TSC: *Option C: Target contract with price list;* and *Option X12: Partnering*
- NEC 3rd edition, PSC (in target cost contracts, where a supplier delivers the works at a cost below the level of the agreed target, the parties share the savings in accordance with a pre-agreed formula): *Option X6: Bonus for early completion* and *Option X12: Partnering;*
- NEC 3rd edition, Engineering and Construction Subcontract: *Option X6: Bonus for early completion;* and *Option X12: Partnering*
- NEC 3rd edition, Engineering and Construction Contract Option F: *Option X: Bonus for early completion*
- NEC 3rd edition, Engineering and Construction Contract Option C: *Option X6: Bonus for early completion;* and *X12: Partnering*
- NEC 3rd edition, Engineering and Construction Contract Option E: *Option X6: Bonus for early completion;* and *X12: Partnering*
- JCT 2005, FA: *Framework Agreement*
- JCT 2005, FA/N: *Framework Agreement Non-Binding*

Target cost contracts

In target costs contracts the sum payable to the contractor depends upon their ability to beat a financial 'target', agreed in advance before the works commence. This type of contract is often used where the extent of the work to be done is not fully defined.

Therefore the contractor accounts for and is paid his actual cost usually with a fee percentage uplift. A final adjustment (up or down) in pre-agreed proportions will then be made dependent upon the amount that the contractor's final actual cost is above or below the target.

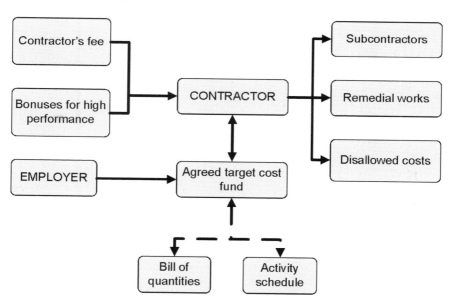

Examples

- NEC 3rd edition, Professional Services Contract: *Option C: Target contract*
- NEC 3rd edition, Engineering and Construction Subcontract, *Option C: Target subcontract with activity schedule*; and *Option D: Target subcontract with bill of quantities*
- NEC 3rd edition, Engineering and Construction Contract: *Option C: Target contract*

Prime cost contract

In a prime cost contract, the contractor is paid the actual or prime cost of carrying out or procuring the identified contract works.

Examples

- JCT 2005, PCC: *Prime Cost Building Contract*
- NEC 3rd edition, Engineering and Construction Subcontract, *Option E: Cost reimbursable subcontract*

Contracts with and without quantities/contracts with approximate quantities

With quantities

In a lump sum contract with quantities, a bill of quantities forms part of the contract and sets out the works to be carried out by the contractor before payment is due. The contractor is often bound to carry out any extra works not specified in the bill, if they are necessary to complete the contract. These works are considered 'extra work' and the contractor is generally entitled to be paid extra for these works.

Example

- JCT 2005, SBC/Q: *Standard Building Contract with Quantities*

Without quantities

In a lump sum contract without quantities, where the agreed works are widely defined, the contractor is obliged to carry out all the necessary works to complete the contract. The works are impliedly included in the lump sum and are not considered 'extra work'.

Example

- JCT 2005, SBC/XQ: *Standard Building Contract without Quantities*

Costs plus a fee (see JCT Management Contract)

In a cost plus fee contract (sometimes called simply 'cost plus contract'), the contractor is paid the actual costs incurred as a result of the agreed contractual works plus a fixed percentage or sum for profit and/or other costs not vouched for.

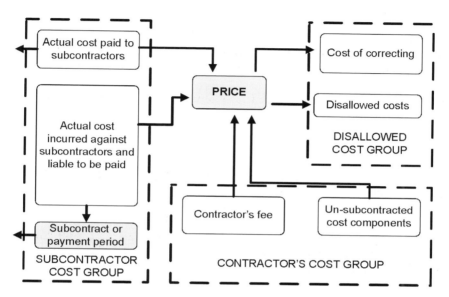

Examples

- JCT 2005, PCC: *Prime Cost Building Contract*
- NEC 3rd edition, Term Service Contract, *Option E: Cost reimbursement contract*
- NEC 3rd edition, Engineering and Construction Contract Option F
- NEC 3rd edition, Engineering and Construction Contract Option E

Certificates and certifiers

The circumstances in which payments become *due* to the party carrying out the works is, subject to the provisions of HGCRA 1996 as they relate to 'construction contracts', a matter for the agreement of the parties. As in any form of commercial contract, one of the important requirements is that there is certainty as to the time at which sums become due, together with certainty as to the amount which is due.

In many fields, payment being due upon performance (delivery of goods) or upon presentation of an invoice (professional services) will be straightforward. Things are less straightforward in the case of substantial long-term construction projects, where cash flow will require interim payments, and the progress of construction will mean that payment-related sanctions will be required to protect against defective or incomplete performance.

A particular feature of the construction industry, and a feature which can often puzzle outsiders, is the frequent use of *certificates* as a 'marker' to identify the occurrence of events, including the occurrence of events giving rise to an entitlement to payment. Typically, the contractor and the employer will agree that sums will become *due* to the contractor upon a third party (architect, quantity surveyor or engineer) issuing a monthly certificate of the value of works and materials properly carried out and/or installed on site. The employer is obliged to pay the amount stated to be due , or else – whether under the contract or under HGCRA 1996 – issue a Notice of Withholding identifying the amount proposed to be withheld and the reasons for the withholding. The next month the certifier will issue a further certificate, which may be higher or lower than the certificate for the previous month, and the obligation to pay – subject to a right to withhold in defined circumstances – arises once again.

Certificates

Most construction contracts expressly require the issue of documents called 'certificates' by the contract administrator. There is no definition of the term, but a certificate is usually taken to embody a decision requiring the exercise of professional skill and judgment on issues which will often require impartial and subjective assessments. The subject matter of certificates and of instructions may overlap, but the latter normally embodies no more than an administrative decision, while the former may involve the initial resolution of a dispute. In *Kaye (P&M) v Hosier & Dickinson* [1972] 1 WLR 146 it was said that the architect:

> ' . . . has to issue certificates showing how much money is owing. Incidentally, his certificates and instructions may resolve some controversial points, and he had to act fairly, but he is not primarily or characteristically adjudicating on disputes.'

Payment certificates may be categorised into interim certificates and final certificates. They will be issued throughout the contract, as required by progress of the works.

Interim certificates

These are the means whereby instalment payments are effected; the most usual arrangement being for monthly valuations to be made on the basis of an approximate measure of work carried out. This will be appropriate whether the contract is for a lump sum or subject to remeasure. In the latter case, however, work will need to be accurately measured as each section is completed, for the purpose of the final account. It was held by the House of Lords in *Gilbert-Ash v Modern Engineering (Bristol) Ltd* [1974] AC 689 that an interim certificate created a debt which could, subject to any contractual term to the contrary, be reduced or extinguished by set-off, reversing decisions of the Court of Appeal to the contrary. An alternative form of interim payments not involving measurement is referred to as 'milestone' payments, whereby the contract sum is divided into predetermined amounts to be released at dates or stages (milestones) of the work. Such payments may, depending on the terms of the contract, require a form of certificate, e.g. as to completion of the requisite work stages. Milestone payments may also be made subject to the achievement of stipulated rates of progress. It has been suggested that payment by milestones will eventually replace interim payments based on monthly measurement. Although the value stated in interim certificates may be corrected in subsequent certificates, the contract administrator will be required to give more than a merely superficial glance at the works prior to the issue of a certificate. Furthermore, where the contract provides for interim payments to be made in respect of 'the total value of the sub-contract work on site properly executed by the sub-contractor' or similar terms, then defective work should not be included in a valuation on the basis that it will be rectified at a later stage.

Final certificate

This is provided for under most construction contracts, although the terminology and the effect of such a certificate will vary between different forms of contract. A final certificate may take effect only as a statement of account but in most cases it also certifies the work as being finally complete. The certificate may also be made conditionally final and binding on the parties as to the opinion of the contract administrator on quality of the work.

There can be recovery without a certificate

It is a matter of construction of the underlying contract whether a certificate is a condition precedent to recovery of the sum of money to be certified. In *Lubenham Fidelities and Investment Co Ltd v South Pembroke DC and Wigley Fox Partnership* (1986) 33 BLR 39 the Court of Appeal held that a certificate issued under the JCT Standard Form of Building Contract, 1963 edition, where there was a patently incorrect deduction, was nevertheless binding, so that the contractor could not assert entitlement to a further sum. May LJ, giving the judgment of the Court held:

> 'Whatever the cause of the undervaluation, the proper remedy available to the contractor is, in our opinion, to request the Architect to make the appropriate adjustment in another certificate, or if he declines to do so, to take the dispute to arbitration under clause 35. In default of arbitration or a new certificate the conditions themselves give the contractor no right to sue for the higher sum. In other words we think that under this form of contract the issue of a certificate is always a condition precedent to the right of the contractor to be paid.'

Most construction contracts now provide a facility for an adjudicator to open up, review and revise payment certificates which will usually now be the proper remedy in the event of under-valuation.

Where the certificate is a condition precedent to recovery of payment, a sum otherwise due may be recovered without a certificate in the following circumstances:

1 where the condition precedent has been waived by the other parties to the contract;
2 where the certifier has been disqualified by improper conduct;
3 where there has been prevention by or on behalf of the employer; and
4 where the certifier becomes incapacitated without being replaced.

In practice, however, it will usually be more convenient to rely on the powers of an arbitrator or adjudicator to review and revise any certificate, which will ordinarily include the power to grant a certificate which has been refused by the certifier. Where the dispute is litigated, the same powers will be available to the court.

Certifiers

Given the practical importance to the contractor of (say) an interim payment certificate, the question which frequently arises is the extent to which the certifier is obliged to act fairly, impartially and independently of the employer. The issue here is complicated because the architect, quantity surveyor or engineer certifying payments is himself usually paid by the employer and there are lots of circumstances within the project where the certifier clearly acts as an agent of the employer (e.g. the instruction of variations to the works).

What, then, is the duty of the architect, quantity surveyor, engineer or other professional when acting in the role of *certifier*? The answer will depend upon an interpretation of terms of the contract in respect of which the professional is carrying out a role as certifier. However, it is clear that the professional is performing two distinct types of function, one of which is *agent* of the employer, and the other – that of certifier – requiring the professional to hold the balance between the contractor and the employer. In more recent decisions, the courts have identified the broad principles involved in this important area.

The Court of Appeal recently considered the authorities in relation to the duties of the certifier in the decision in *Amec Civil Engineering Ltd v Secretary of State for Transport* [2005] EWCA Civ 291. In that case (which was an unsuccessful appeal from a decision and order of the TCC) the appellant sought to contend that the engineer under an amended version of the ICE Conditions, 5th edition, owed duties akin to obligations to observe the rules of natural justice. This contention was rejected, but from the judgments of both May LJ and Rix LJ, it is plain that the certifier *did* have obligations of fairness, independence and impartiality.

Thus:

1   in paragraph 38 of his judgment (see p. 236, second column), May LJ referred to the decision in *Hounslow LBC v Twickenham Garden Developments* [1971] Ch 233 and summarised Megarry J's conclusions as being that the certifying architect was 'obliged to retain his independence in exercising his judgment' but need not observe the rules of natural justice unless the contract so provided;

2   in paragraph 40 of his judgment (see p. 237, first column), May LJ referred to the decision in *AC Hatrick (NZ) Ltd v Nelson Carlton Construction Co Ltd* [1964] NZLR 72 and said: 'The essence of these passages is that an architect or engineer acting as a certifier has to exercise an honest and independent judgment ...';

3   the authorities are the subject of review in paragraphs 78–81 of the judgment of Rix LJ (see pp. 242 and 243) with the summary in paragraph 81 being particularly informative, it is submitted: (a) the engineer must 'retain his independence in exercising [his skilled professional] Judgment' (Megarry J in *Hounslow* at 259G); (b) he must 'act in a fair and unbiased manner' and 'reach his decisions fairly, holding the balance' (Lord Reid in *Sutcliffe v Thackrah* [1974] AC 727 at 737D); (c) he must 'act fairly' (Lord Morris in *Sutcliffe v Thackrah* at 744G); significantly (d) if he hears representations from one party, he must give a similar opportunity to the other party to answer what is alleged against him (*AC Hatrick*); and (e) he must 'act fairly and impartially' where fairness is 'a broad and even elastic concept' and impartiality 'is not meant to be a narrow concept' (Cooke J in *Canterbury Pipe Lines Ltd v Christchurch Draining Board* [1979] 16 BLR 76 NZCA);

4   in another recent decision in *Scheldebouw BV v St James Homes (Grosvenor Dock) Ltd* [2006] EWHC 89 (TCC), Jackson J reviewed these same authorities and said this (at   paragraph 34):

> 'Three propositions emerge from the authorities concerning the position of the decision-maker.
>
> (1)   The precise role and duties of the decision-maker will be determined by the terms of the contract under which he is required to act.
>
> (2)   Generally the decision-maker is not, and cannot be regarded as, independent of the employer.
>
> (3)   When performing his decision-making function, the decision-maker is required to act in a manner which   has   variously   been   described   as

independent, impartial, fair and honest. These concepts are overlapping but not synonymous. They connote that the decision-maker must use his professional skills and his best endeavours to reach the right decision, as opposed to a decision which favours the interests of the employer ...'

Frequently asked questions

Q. Does a payment certificate create a debt due?

A. It used to be thought that a payment certificate created a debt, allowing the client to set-off only in very limited circumstances. It is now clear, however, that where HGCRA 1996 applies and provided the client issues his withholding notice on time the client can set-off from the sum due for any number of reasons. The situation regarding contracts that fall outside the scope of HGCRA 1996 is governed by the decision of the House of Lords in *Gilbert-Ash Ltd v Modern Engineering (Bristol) Ltd* [1974] AC 689, HL where they held that unless the contract states otherwise the client can rely on breaches of contract by the contractor in diminution or extinction of a sum certified by the architect.

Q. Can a contractor suspend works when he believes that a payment certificate under-values his works?

A. If the contract provides for the payment certificate to be issued by a third party such as an architect then it has been held that the employer's only liability is to pay the sum certified. See *Lubenham Fidelities and Investment Co Ltd v South Pembrokeshire DC and Wigley Fox Partnership* (1986) 33 BLR 39 at 55, CA. In these circumstances it cannot be argued that by paying the sum certified the client has failed to pay the sum due. Therefore the contractor's remedy is to seek to amend the certificate in adjudication or arbitration or litigation. However, where the certificate is invalid (such as where the employer has interfered with the certification process) or where there is no independent certifier then the employer's payment obligation may well extend beyond paying the sum certified. Therefore if the sum certified does not represent the value of works done then the contractor may have a right to suspend performance in addition to his rights to have the certificate reviewed.

4

The right to interim payments

Introduction

One of the primary obligations of the employer is to pay the contractor for work undertaken in performance of the contract. Clearly, many construction contracts last for years and it is common for the contract to provide for a series of interim payments to be made as the work progresses.

The mechanisms for this evolved through contract drafting during the last century. However, whilst this book is not focused on the *Housing Grants, Construction and Regeneration Act* 1996 (HGCRA 1996), the massive impact that those statutory provisions have had on payments in construction contracts in the UK cannot be ignored.

The right to payment

In general terms the parties to a contract are free to enter into whatever arrangements they wish with regard to payments. However, since the coming into force of HGCRA 1996 on 1 May 1998, this is no longer true. The freedom of contract for parties to a construction contract (to which this book is primarily aimed) is now fettered by a fundamental requirement to comply with the provisions of s. 109–113 of HGCRA 1996.

Where HGCRA 1996 does not apply and there are no contractual provisions governing a right to interim payments the inference of an applied right is governed by the usual rules of implied terms but it has been stated that:

> '... a man who contracts to do a long costly piece of work does not contract, unless he expressly says so that

he will do all the work, standing out of pocket until he is paid at the end. He is entitled to say "there is an understanding all along that you are to give me from time to time, at the reasonable times, payment for work done".' See Phillimore J in *The Tergeste* [1903] LR p. 26 at 34.

This appears to imply stage payments or interim payments on a contract which neither falls within the ambit of the Act nor has an express entire agreement clause.

Entire contracts

An entire contract is one by which entire performance by one party is a condition precedent on the obligation of the other to pay the contract sum. Clear and express words are required to form an entire contract and in such contracts there is usually no entitlement to interim payment until such time as the contractor's entire performance is completed. In the rare circumstances of an entire contract (subject to compliance with HGCRA 1996) then a failure by the contractor to fully satisfy the requirements of the contract in full may result in no entitlement to any payment whatsoever. However, as stated above, the incidence of entire contracts in the construction industry which do not provide for interim or instalment payments is rare, and in some circumstances the payment mechanism will not be deemed adequate in accordance with HGCRA 1996.

Section 109 of HGCRA 1996 provides that there is a statutory entitlement to payment by instalments, stage payments or other periodic payments in certain construction contracts.

Where this section does apply (i.e. in contracts in excess of 45 days), if the parties have not agreed the amounts of the payments and the intervals at which, or the circumstances in which, they become due paragraphs 2–4 of Part II of the Scheme for Construction Contracts provide for the amount of the payments to be made by way of instalments and the dates by which those payments are to be made.

The amount of payment is calculated either by reference to the provisions of the contract or, where there are no such provisions, by reference to the value of the works (paragraph 2).

Value is defined as 'the cost of any work performed in accordance with the contract together with the amounts equal to any overhead or profit included in the contract price' (paragraph 12).

The due date for payment is the later of 'the expiry of 7 days following the relevant period' or the making of a claim by the payee (paragraph 4).

The Housing Grants, Construction and Regeneration Act 1996

The limits of HGCRA 1996

Many construction contracts will fall within the ambit of HGCRA 1996 which are covered in detail in Chapter 8. However, there is a broad class of contracts which are specifically excluded from the implications of the Act.

Contract administrator certifier

The term 'contract administrator certifier' applies to the situation where a third party (an architect, surveyor, engineer or other construction professional) has been instructed to perform the role of contract administrator and to certify the amount of interim payments. This is the normal prevailing position for standard forms of contract. However, a large proportion of the disputes in construction contracts, and arising out of such contracts, arise on subcontracts, some forms of design and build contract and ad hoc forms of contract when no independent certifier exists.

Under these circumstances where there is no independent certifier the question arises: what is the entitlement to payment in the absence of a withholding notice?

It is a common misconception that, in the absence of a withholding notice, the payee is entitled to be paid the amount which is claimed under the contract in the absence of express terms to that effect.

No third party certification

No third party certification was the background to the case of *SL Timber Systems v Carillion Construction Ltd* [2001] BLR 516. The application for payment was an invoice submitted by the contractor. The contract did not provide for interim payments to be measured, valued and certified by the contract administrator. The defence of the employer in the adjudication was to defend the claim by arguing that the contractor's invoice did not make the 'sum due under the contract'. What was due was the work that had been done. Work not done and not due for payment required no withholding notice. The adjudicator was therefore required to ask what was due. This could involve abating the contract price and the contractor's invoice to take account of defective works and works not in accordance with the contract, i.e. works where the payment was not entitled to be made but would preclude setting-off sums. Setting-off sums, i.e. liquidated damages, counterclaim, set-off, etc. would require a withholding notice. The situation can be summarised as follows: where there is an independent certifier, if the certificate is validly issued then the paying party, the employer, must pay what is on the face of the certificate unless he has served a section 111 Notice of Intention to Withhold. He cannot abate from the certified sum or set-off without this notice.

Where there is no independent certifier then the contractor is merely entitled to be paid the amount due under the contract, i.e. the amount for works properly executed. The contractor's invoice or subcontract price can be abated for defective works but in the absence of a section 111 withholding notice no set-off or counterclaim can be used to reduce the amount due.

Set-off and abatement

There are three ways in which a party may seek to reduce the amount he is due to pay:

1   common law set-off;
2   equitable set-off; and
3   abatement.

Common law set-off developed from the 18th-century statutes of set-off. It is a procedural device to avoid multiple cross-claims by which a party can show, in his defence, that he has valid claims against his creditors that should be set off against the amount due from him. Equitable set-off developed from the equitable principles of unconscionability. It applies to a broader field of demands (i.e. including those that might not in themselves give rise to an action) and in effect prevents a creditor suing for the price of goods/services where his title to those goods/services is somehow defective (usually by virtue of the goods/services being defective). Abatement is a common-law remedy, so is available as of right and not subject to discretion. It operates similarly to equitable set-off, allowing a debtor to show that the goods/services claimed are not worth the amount that the creditor claims. Several recent cases indicate that the courts will treat equitable set-off and abatement as synonymous.

In *Northern Developments (Cumbria) Ltd v J&J Nichol* [2000] BLR 158, it was held that where HGCRA 1996 applies the adjudicator should not take set-off into account where the other party had not issued a valid notice to withhold. The question that therefore arises is: can the losing party raise the defence of set-off after the adjudicator's decision but before payment has been made? It was held in *VHE Construction plc v RBSTB Trust Co Ltd* [2000] BLR 187 that it could not do so. Where a party has failed to comply with section 110 in raising a notice of intention to withhold payment it could raise the matter when first responding to the adjudication, but could not set-off after the decision is made. This goes to the root of adjudication being a means of enforcing cash flow which can be summarily enforced.

However, there have been circumstances where there is an entitlement to withhold monies against a valid adjudicator's award. These are based on the contract terms. In the case of *Shimizu Europe Ltd v LBJ Fabrications Ltd* [2003] EWHC 1229 (TCC), the contract provided that no payment was due until the contractor had supplied a valid VAT invoice in the correct amount to the employer. The parties adjudicated on a variation account and the adjudicator held that there were sums for which Shimizu was entitled to invoice. However, even though Shimizu subsequently issued a valid VAT invoice, LBJ Fabrications issued a withholding notice against that saying that they were entitled to do so as it was in the contractual terms.

The Court held that in such circumstances no monies had become due until the issue of the VAT invoice and as such the contract provisions entitling set-off prevailed.

The question of set-off has long been a bone of contention. In general, it appears that there is a right of set-off unless, looking at the contract as a whole, it is excluded expressly or by necessary implication. The point is important because, at one time, the architect's certificate was considered as good as cash and had to be honoured. It now seems clear, however, that provided the employer has good grounds he can withhold payment on a certificate and, resisting summary judgment, go to arbitration or trial. This is bad news for contractors, particularly because it appears that the employer need only show that there are reasonable grounds to challenge the certificate.

Following the HGCRA 1996, all major forms of contracts contain express provisions to deal with set-off or, as the contracts now refer to it, withholding or deduction. Because the provisions were inserted as a result of legislation, they are substantially the same in all contracts.

The employer must issue a written notice to the contractor within five days of the due date for payment. In the JCT contracts this is the date of issue of each payment certificate (including the final certificate) except the JCT 2005, *Design and Build Contract* (JCT DB 2005) where the due date for payment is the date of receipt of an application for payment or from the date the final account and final statement become conclusive. The notice must state the amount which the employer proposes to pay, to what it relates and how it is calculated. Presumably, the notice will state the amount in the certificate although it is possible, but not certain, that the employer could use the opportunity to abate the sum (i.e. to reduce it, possibly because work has not been done). If the employer wishes to withhold or deduct any amount from the sum due including abatement, he must issue a written notice not later than (usually) five days before the final date for payment of any certificate (or application under JCT DB 2005). This notice must state the grounds for withholding and the amount to be withheld for each ground. If the employer does not give a written notice in accordance with one and/or both provisions, he must pay the sum in full. Under HGCRA 1996 the first notice will suffice for both if it indicates a deduction and sets out the grounds in sufficient detail. It appears from the wording that the contractual position may be the same, whether 1 or 2 notices are issued but it would generally be advisable for the employer to give both notices if wishing to deduct any amounts. Obviously, the employer who intends to pay the full amount may omit to give any notices. He would technically be in breach but, provided he paid in full, the contractor could hardly complain. It is now established that the amount due under JCT DB 2005 if no withholding notice is served is the amount in the application. This is clear from clause 4.10.6. See also *VHE Construction plc*.

The JCT contracts provide that the employer must pay simple interest at 5 per cent above the Bank of England Base Rate if he fails to pay the amount due by the final date for payment. This is in addition to the contractor's other rights to suspend or determine or, in appropriate cases, to accept repudiation under the general law.

Frequently asked questions

Q. What are the practical consequences of the legal distinction between set-off and abatement?

A. Where HGCRA 1996 applies, set-off requires a section 111 withholding notice whereas abatement does not. Abatement should be included in the section 110 payment notice but is available to the paying party even in the absence of such a notice.

Q. What sums can be set-off from payment certificates?

A. The client's right of set-off is dependent on the terms of the contract. In the absence of any such terms the default common law position is very complex and divides into two lines of authority. On the one hand there is authority for the strict proposition that the cross-claim has to raise an equity in the defendant's favour which impeached the plaintiff's title to the claim. See *Rawson v Samuel* (1841) cr & Ph 161 at 179. In other words the claim which forms the set-off has to be very closely related to the principal claim. There is an alternative more liberal proposition that suggests that set-off is available provided that both claims arise from the same contract. This distinction is more important in adjudication than in litigation because unlike a judge, an adjudicator's jurisdiction is usually limited to a single dispute arising from a single contract. Therefore an adjudicator can take set-off into account in a dispute over amounts due but will not be able to take into account counterclaims that do not fall within the scope of set-off.

Interim certificates

These certificates are issued from time to time during the course of the works certifying that, in the opinion of the architect, work has been carried out and in some cases materials supplied to the value of £X.

The approach of the courts to such certificates can be seen from the following decisions

Secretary of State for Transport v Birse-Farr Joint Venture [1993] 62 BLR 36

> 'Certification may be a complex exercise involving an exercise of judgment and an investigation and assessment of potential conflicts and voluminous material. An assessment by an engineer of the appropriate interim payment made can have a margin of error either way ...'

At the interim stage it cannot be a wholly exact exercise. It must include an element of assessment and judgment. Its purpose is not to produce a final determination of the remuneration to which the contractor was entitled but is to provide a fair system of monthly progress payments to be made to the contractor.

Henry Boot Construction Ltd v Alstom Combined Cycles Ltd [2005] EWCA Civ 814

> 'The nature of the exercise required by the contract to be performed by the engineer at an interim stage is so different from that required at final account stage ...
>
> It seems to me that the submission of Counsel (for the employer) failed to take account of the fundamental differences between what the engineer is required to do at an interim stage and what he is required to do at the final stage. The position would be otherwise if this were, say, a contract for a fixed sum of £1m whose only payment provision is that the price was to be paid by 10 equal monthly instalments of a £100,000 ...
>
> The right to payment of £100,000 for that work would be unaffected by any other provisions of the contract. It would not be reviewed or recalculated at the end of the

contract. But this kind of contractual arrangement is quite different from that provided by the contract in this case [ICE 5th edition]. The contract provides elaborate provisions for dealing with instalment payments on account and a very different set of elaborate provisions for ascertaining the contract price and final payment in the light of the work actually done and the events that occurred in carrying out the works.'

It is clear from these two cases that interim certificates are merely estimates made for the purposes of determining how much the employer is required to pay in advance for the completion of the works where he is under a duty to pay in instalments.

Such certificates are not normally binding on the parties as to the quality of work done or the computation of the final payment, for example the valuation of adjustments to the contract price may be subject to reduction on completion. They have been variously described as having a 'provisional validity' or being 'provisional estimates of the sum which the contractor is entitled by way of instalment payments'. The sum certified is not necessarily the true final value of the work done and materials supplied.

Any error in an interim certificate can be and should be corrected in the next certificate. The contractor may also have a remedy for interest for late payment as damages for breach of an express implied term of the contract, if the certifier has failed to issue certificates at the proper times or for the correct sums. Since the introduction of adjudication under HGCRA 1996 this offers a further remedy for under valuation.

Care is needed where there is an independent certifier. Provided that the employer has not interfered with or prevented the independent certifier from fulfilling his role the employer's only obligation is to pay the sum certified. Contractual and statutory provisions for interest on late payment would not usually apply where there has been under-certification in such cases provided that the employer has paid the sum certified by the final date for payment.

At common law an employer who has a bona fide arguable contention that an interim certificate over-values the contractor's right to payment can resist proceedings for summary judgment on those grounds.

Interim payments under the JCT

Summary

The procedure for preparing valuations for interim certificates must be based on the procedure set out in the relevant contract. Procedures for payment by milestone are becoming more common, but the traditional route of payment for work done is still the most popular procedure.

Assessing amounts due

The method of valuation that is adopted for an interim certificate should always follow the scheme set down in the relevant contract.

JCT Standard Building Contract 2005

The JCT Standard Building Contract 2005 (SBC) offers the parties an opportunity to agree to stage payments – i.e. payment by way of agreed milestones. However, in the event that there is no such agreement the contract defaults to a valuation of work done at predetermined intervals.

The value of work done is the employer's principal security for payments made. It is often said that the time-lag between valuation and payment, and the availability of other securities, such as performance bonds, will more than compensate for any over-valuation. Therefore, the valuation of work done need not be too accurate. However, this logic fails to recognise that the employer will need all of that additional security to compensate him for the losses that he is bound to incur in the event of contractor insolvency prior to completion. If the amount of security available to the employer is reduced because of an overly generous valuation, the employer may try to seek compensation from his consultants.

It is therefore important that valuations for interim certificates are reasonably accurate although they need not be precise.

In *Secretary of State for Transport v Birse-Farr Joint Venture* [1993] 62 BLR 36 it was alleged that there had been a failure by the engineer to certify because it was found that the amounts due in interim payments should have been higher than the engineer had certified. The Court held that certification may be a complex exercise and as such may have a margin of error either way. Its purpose is not to produce a final determination of the remuneration to which the contractor is entitled, but to provide a fair system of monthly progress payments to be made to the contractor. Simply to assert that sums subsequently awarded were not included in earlier certificates does not, in itself, prove a failure to certify in accordance with the terms of the contract.

Under the SBC the contract administrator is required to issue interim certificates stating the amount due to the contractor from the employer. Unless the parties have agreed to payment by milestones the amount due must be calculated by reference to the gross valuation from which may be deducted retention, any advance payments made and any amounts previously certified as due.

The gross valuation is calculated to include the following:

1   the total value of work properly executed. This is calculated by reference to the contract bills or other priced document or, where there is an activity schedule, by reference to that schedule. The value of any variations and the value of any fluctuations calculated by way of formula adjustment are also included;
2   the total value of unfixed goods and materials delivered to the works;
3   the total value of listed items (which are goods and materials described as such and included in a list annexed to the contract bills) which belong to the contractor, are ready for delivery to the works but are stored at premises remote from the works;
4   various payments made or costs incurred by the contractor such as under the insurance provisions, royalties, patents, rates or taxes, tests instructed by the contract administrator (other than where those tests show goods or work are not in accordance with the contract);
5   loss and expense which the contractor has incurred by reason of:
      (a) antiquities being found on the site;
      (b) variations to the contract;
      (c) instructions of the contract administrator to postpone any of the works;
      (d) instructions of the contract administrator to expend provisional sums (other than provisional sums for defined works);

    (e) instructions by the contract administrator to open up work for inspection (other than where that inspection shows goods or work are not in accordance with the contract);

    (f) instructions of the contract administrator in relation to any discrepancy or divergences between the contract drawings, the contract bills (or other priced document) and any instructions of the contract administrator;

    (g) suspension by the contractor due to his not having been paid in full by the final date for payment;

    (h) approximate quantities not being a reasonably accurate forecast of the quantity of work required; and

    (i) any impediment, prevention of default by or on behalf of the employer or any of the consultants employed by the employer;

6   where the employer insures the works, any restoration, replacement or repair of any loss or damage including the removal and disposal of debris;

7   any amount payable (or refundable) by way of fluctuations (other than fluctuations calculated by way of formula adjustment);

8   less any appropriate deduction for errors in setting out by the contractor; work, materials or goods not being in accordance with the contract; or any defect, shrinkage or other fault which appears in the rectification period and which the contract administrator instructs shall not be amended or made good; and

9   less any additional costs incurred by the employer in employing others to undertake works following failure by the contractor to comply with an instruction of the contract administrator.

The retention is calculated as a percentage of the total value of work properly executed, the total value of unfixed goods and materials and the total value of listed items included within the gross valuation.

The retention percentage is reduced by half in respect of any work that has reached practical completion including any section or any part of the works of which the employer wishes and contractor consents to the employer taking early possession.

No retention may be withheld in respect of any part of the works for which a certificate of making good has been issued.

Paying agreed sums for completed milestones

For milestone payments (or stage payments as they are referred to in the SBC) payment will fall due at whatever stages the parties have agreed. Often the parties will agree that the payment is not due until particular milestones have been achieved. In this case no money is due for a part-completed milestone. Milestones therefore need to be drafted and interpreted carefully. For example, no money will be due against a milestone for 'painting' until all of the touching-up has been completed, despite the fact that preparation and priming may have commenced many months before. Milestones therefore need to be designed to achieve cash-flow expectations without causing an unnecessary administrative burden.

Payments against milestones can become extremely tiresome unless the procedure is linked to periodic assessments (e.g. at the end of each month). Otherwise, different milestones could be achieved one day after another, leading to a flurry of invoices and payments.

Withholding money

Under the SBC the amount due in each interim certificate takes into consideration the amount stated as due in the previous interim certificate. Note that it is the sum certified that is relevant and not the sum paid. Therefore if the employer withholds a sum against an interim certificate (e.g. for liquidated damages) the employer does not need to issue withholding notices in respect of that sum for future interim certificates. Clearly, however, if the employer wishes to increase the amount being withheld or to withhold additional sums then further withholding notices for those additional sums will be required.

Where sums are to be withheld by the employer, such as liquidated damages, these sums should not be deducted from the value stated on the interim certificate. The employer must deduct the relevant sums separately after the interim certificate has been issued. The employer will need to issue a withholding notice at the correct time and in the correct form in order to deduct sums. This notice must be issued by the employer. It cannot be issued by the contract administrator on his behalf, although the employer may well seek the advice of the contract administrator with regard to the form and timing of the notice.

Provisional validity of interim valuations

Under the SBC, valuations for interim payments are deemed to be fresh calculations for each certificate, even if in practice they are frequently based on the previous valuation. Therefore, the inclusion or calculation of any item as part of the valuation in one month does not prevent the surveyor from omitting that item or including a different calculation for it in a subsequent valuation. In *Beaufort Developments (NI) Ltd v Gilbert-Ash (NI) Ltd* [1999] 1 AC 266, HL, interim certificates were described as having provisional validity.

Duties of the contract administrator

The key objective of the contract administrator should be to value the works reasonably accurately, so as not to expose the parties to unnecessary risk in the event of failure or insolvency of the other party, and so as not to impose on the contractor a higher level of project financing than is necessary.

The contract administrator should follow the contractual procedures as closely as possible.

Although *Lubenham v South Pembrokeshire DC* [1986] 33 BLR 39, CA is a case related to arbitration it is authority for the principle that where there are wide rights by which the contractor can challenge the decision of the contract administrator (e.g. through adjudication), a contractor will rarely have any significant reason subsequently to complain that certificates were not issued in accordance with the contract.

Duties of the contractor

Some contracts require the contractor to assist the contract administrator in valuing the interim payments. Even where the contract does not provide for this, it will usually be in the contractor's interests to do so.

The SBC gives the contractor an option to submit an application for payment but preparation of the interim certificate by the contract administrator is not conditional on such an application being received. The SBC provides that if the contractor wishes to submit an application for payment he must do so not later than seven days before the date when the interim certificate is to be issued.

Payment for materials and plant

Ownership of valuable materials, particularly those stored off site, becomes a hotly contested issue in the event of insolvency. The client will often have paid for the materials and will therefore be seeking title; the company receiver will often be in possession of the materials and will therefore be seeking title; and the initial supplier may not have been paid for the materials, and will therefore also be seeking title.

The general rule is that title to goods will pass upon their delivery, regardless of whether or not they have been paid for (see the *Sale of Goods Act* 1979 and the *Supply of Goods and Services Act* 1982 as amended). However, this general rule can be modified by the terms of the supply contract and usually is.

SBC provides that title in goods and materials passes to the employer where their value has been included in an interim certificate and the amount properly due under that interim certificate has been paid by the employer.

Many suppliers will include terms in their contracts such that title does not pass until payment is received by the supplier, regardless of delivery or payment to the contractor. These type of clauses are often referred to as 'retention of title' clauses.

There is a lot of case law and a fair amount of legislation surrounding retention of title clauses. The basic principles are that, subject to the following, retention of title clauses are valid to deprive the client of title, even though the client may have paid a third party (the insolvent contractor) for the goods (see *Aluminium Industrie Vaassen v Romalpa Aluminium* [1976]):

- under contracts for the supply of goods (not generally including construction contracts, which are usually contracts for the supply of goods and services), a seller in possession of goods with the consent of the owner may pass good title to those goods, despite the existence of a retention of title clause (see the *Sale of Goods Act* 1979);
- a right to goods will be lost where those goods have been irretrievably mixed or incorporated into other goods, despite

the existence of a retention of title clause. For this reason, it was found that a retention of title clause over resin used in the manufacture of chipboard was ineffective (*Borden (UK) v Scottish Timber* [1981]), but a retention of title clause over an engine that had been bolted to a concrete slab was still effective, as the engine could be unbolted (*Hendy Lennox v Grahame Puttick* [1984]);

- depending on the terms of the retention of title clause, it may have effect as a floating charge over the property. If this is the case, then in respect of limited companies, that charge needs to be registered at Companies House if it is to have effect as against third parties.

Special care is therefore required to check that the contractor has good title to goods when including the value of unfixed materials in interim payments, especially where those goods are of high value or are stored off site. Simply asking the contractor will not be sufficient – and neither will asking his subcontractor as the retention of title clause may go further down the supply chain. To be sure of the good transfer of title, it will be necessary to check down the supply chain until a contract for the supply of goods by a seller in possession of those goods who claims to have good unencumbered title to those goods is identified, or a manufacturing process irretrievably incorporating or mixing the goods is found. The proper transfer of title should then be traced from this point up.

Extra special care is required when making payment for materials from abroad that have not yet been delivered into England. The insolvency laws of other legal jurisdictions are different to those of England, and generally override any contractual provisions. Payment for materials stored outside the jurisdiction of the English courts should only by made against an on-demand bond given by a reputable bank with a sizeable presence in England.

Contractor's entitlement to interest for under-valuation

Generally, standard forms of contract such as the SBC do not provide the contractor with a contractual right to recover interest for under-valuation. Interest provisions in the standard forms are generally restricted to late payment against certificates, rather than under-valuation in the certificates themselves. Therefore, interest for such under-valuation is extra-contractual and cannot be considered as a payment due under the contract.

With the statutory right of adjudication available to correct any alleged under-valuation, contractors' claims for such interest should be very limited (see *Lubenham v South Pembrokeshire DC* (1986) 6 Con LR 85).

Issuing the certificate

Only the person authorised by the contract to do so may issue interim certificates. Special attention must be paid to this point during periods of absence, or if the appointment of the authorised person is terminated by the employer.

Interim certificates must be issued on the dates provided in the contract particulars.

Not later than five days after the issue of the interim certificate the employer shall give a written notice to the contractor stating the amount of the payment proposed to be made to what the amount relates and the basis on which that amount was calculated. This notice requirement can usually be fulfilled simply by referring to the interim certificate and forwarding a copy of the valuation prepared by the contract administrator or quantity surveyor (or referring to it if previously forwarded). However, under the SBC, there are no sanctions if the employer fails to produce this notice on time or even at all and provided that the contractor has received a copy of the valuation and a copy of the interim certificate there seems to be little to be gained from an additional notice issued by the employer.

The final date for payment is 14 days from the date of issue of the interim certificate.

If the employer wishes to withhold money from sums that would otherwise be due to the contractor under the interim certificate the employer must issue a notice to that effect not later than five days before the final date for payment. That notice must state the amount proposed to be withheld, the ground or grounds for such withholding and the amount being withheld attributable to each ground. If the employer does not issue a withholding notice at the right time and in the right form he will not be able to withhold money from the sums that would otherwise fall due for payment.

JCT Intermediate Building Contract 2005

The JCT Intermediate Building Contract 2005 (IC) adopts a similar scheme to interim certificates as the SBC save that the equivalent provisions to retention operate by way of a percentage of the gross valuation that is payable (e.g. 95 per cent) rather than as a percentage of the gross valuation to be retained.

JCT Minor Works Building Contract 2005

The JCT Minor Works Building Contract 2005 (MW) simplifies matters enormously but essentially adopts a similar scheme to the SBC and IC.

The principal differences between the MW and the other forms are as follows:

1   Interim certificates are referred to as progress payments. The certificate for progress payments is due at intervals of four weeks calculated from the date of commencement of the works.
2   The MW does not expressly invite the contractor to submit an application for payment but there is nothing to stop him from doing so anyway.
3   There is no provision for listed items.
4   There is no provision for including other payments or costs incurred by the contractor.
5   There is no provision for including loss and expense.
6   There is no provision for the employer insuring the works.
7   There is no provision for fluctuations.
8   There is no provision to deduct an allowance for accepted defects or additional costs incurred by the employer in instructing others (these deductions can only be made in the final certificate or by way of a withholding notice).
9   The equivalent provisions to retention operate in a similar way to the IC except that the percentage payable applies to the whole gross valuation.

JCT Design and Build Contract 2005

The JCT Design and Build Contract 2005 (DB) adopts quite a different scheme to the other JCT forms.

DB offers two alternative procedures for ascertaining the gross valuation. Referred to as alternative A and alternative B these are payment by milestones (alternative A) or valuation of work properly executed (alternative B). The SBC and the IC do refer to the possibility of the parties agreeing to payment by way of stages (alternative A equivalent) but there is no equivalent mechanism to the alternative A mechanism in the DB.

Alternative B in the DB requires a gross valuation to be calculated in a similar form to the SBC.

The principal difference between the DB and the SBC is the procedure by which the application and valuation is to be made. Under the DB the contractor makes an application for interim payment either on the completion of each stage (alternative A) or on the dates provided for in the contract particulars (alternative B) accompanied by such details as are stated in the employer's requirements.

Receipt by the employer of the contractor's application for interim payment is a pre-condition to interim payments falling due.

Not later than five days after receipt by the employer of the contractor's application for interim payment, the employer shall give a written notice to the contractor stating the amount of the payment proposed to be made, to what the amount relates and the basis on which that amount was calculated.

Unlike the SBC this notice is very important because if it is not issued in time or in the correct form the contractor is entitled to be paid the amount that it has included in the contractor's application for interim payment.

The final date for payment is 14 days from the date of receipt by the employer of the contractor's application for interim payment.

Frequently asked questions

Q. When calculating the gross valuation can the contract administrator reduce an allowance made in previous interim certificates for variations or loss and expense?

A. Yes. Each calculation of the gross valuation is a fresh calculation and therefore allowances made in previous interim certificates can be adjusted up or down if the contract administrator believes that the previous allowance was incorrect or if more information is available. However, a downward adjustment of a previous allowance should not be made lightly as the contractor may well have used that previous valuation as the basis of his own valuations for payment of his subcontractors.

Q. Does the contract administrator have to issue a retention statement for all JCT forms?

A. No. A retention statement is only referred to in SBC. However, all of the forms require the employer to issue a notice stating the amount of the payment proposed to be made, to what the amount relates and the basis on which that amount was calculated. This notice requirement necessarily requires the employer to state how the retention has been calculated or to which parts of the gross valuation different percentages have been applied.

Q. Under DB if the employer misses the date for issuing the payment notice can it challenge the amount applied for in the contractor's application for interim payment in adjudication?

A. No. However, if the contractor is dishonestly claiming for money that it knows that it is not entitled to be paid the employer can challenge the contractor's right to payment in court.

Interim payments under the NEC

As described above the NEC provides a wholly different make up from the more 'traditional' contract. This extends to interim payments. Interim payments are provided for in section 5 of the core clauses of the NEC3 and the particular provisions are:

- Clause 50 – assessing the amount due;
- Clause 51 – payment; and
- Clause 52 – defined costs.

However, the NEC3 states that a contract can be 'built up' from the option, sub-options and secondary options. These options are as follows:

1   Option X1 – price adjustment for inflation;
2   Option X3 – multiple currencies;

3 Option X14 – advance payments; and
4 Option X16 – retention.

Despite these various options the essential features of the interim payment provisions are common to the six main options and are as follows:

1 Assessments of amounts due are made at not more than five weekly intervals (as stated in the contract data). Certification is within one week of each assessment date (clause 51.1), payment is due within three weeks of each assessment date, unless stated otherwise.
2 Interest is due on late certification, under-certification or late payment (clauses 51.2 and 51.3).

Amounts due

The rules for calculating amounts due on both interim and final payments vary according to the main option used. In short, subject to specific adjustments under the X clauses, the amounts due are as follows.

Option A – Priced contract with activities schedule

● Interim amounts – the total of prices for complete activities.
● The final amount – the total prices of the activities.

Option B – Priced contract with bill of quantities

● Interim amounts – the quantities of completed works at bill of quantity rates and proportions of any lump sums.
● Final amount – remeasured value of the work in accordance with the bill of quantities.

Option C – Target contract with activity schedule

● Interim amounts – defined costs/defined costs plus fee.
● Final amount – tendered price as per the activity schedule plus or minus the contractor's share.

Option D – Target contract with bill of quantities

● Interim amount – defined cost plus fee.
● Final amount – remeasured value of the work in accordance with the bill of quantities plus or minus contractor's share.

Option E – Cost reimbursable contract

- Interim account – defined cost plus fee.
- Final amount – defined cost plus fee.

Option F – Management contract

- Interim account – defined cost plus fee.
- Final amount – defined cost plus fee.

Under the NEC payment mechanism the burden of assessing the amount due falls on the project manager. This is an obligation on the project manager irrespective of whether or not the contractor submits a monthly 'valuation'.

For Option A assessment of the amounts due is a straightforward matter of deciding which activities have been completed. It is the obligation of the project manager to do this. If they are not completed as defined in the contract, then no payment is due.

However, for other options, particularly those where interim payments are based on the defined costs then the assessment process can be time-consuming and complex. In accordance with clause 51.1 the project manager is only allowed one week to make his assessment and is likely to need plentiful support staff or the services of a professional quantity surveying firm to assist.

Assessing the amount due

The contractor can make application for payment and if he does so the project manager has to consider this in his assessment. However, at clause 51.1 the project manager is required to issue a certificate within one week of the assessment date regardless of whether an application has been made or not. The first assessment date is decided by the project manager to suit procedures of the parties but must not be later than the assessment interval after the starting date. It is usually one month. In the contract data it is indicated that the assessment interval should be no more than five weeks so the first assessment date should be no more than five weeks after the starting point. This is again subject to option X14 – that the advanced payments option is not being used.

Defined cost

'Defined cost' is a defined term found in:

1   clause 11.2(22) for options A and B;
2   clause 11.2(23) for options C, D and E;
3   clause 11.2(24) for option F.

Although defined cost only forms the full basis of the contractor's entitlement to payment under the cost reimbursable options E and F, it is of considerable importance in options A and B for the assessment of compensation events and in options C and D for compensation events and cost sharing calculations.

Clause 52.1

Clause 52.1 states certain matters common to usage of defined cost. The first provision of the clause states that all the contractor's costs not included within defined cost are deemed to be included in the fee. In other words, the contractor must allow, in the fee percentages which he tenders in part two of the contract data, for all costs not expressly covered within the definition of defined cost.

The second provision of clause 52.1 states that defined costs include only:

1   amounts calculated using rates and percentages stated in the contract data, and other amounts;
2   at open market or competitively tendered prices with deduction of all discounts, rebates and taxes which can be recovered.

The application of this provision is not free from practical difficulties but it goes some way towards protecting the employer from the excesses which sometimes tarnish cost plus contracts.

Clause 10.5 – payments – main option A

The following core payment clauses are particular to main option A – the prices contract with activity schedule:

1   clause 11.2(20) – definition of activity schedule;
2   clause 11.2(22) – definition of defined cost;

3   clause 11.2(27) – definition of price for work done to date;
4   clause 11.2(30) – definition of the prices;
5   clause 54.1 – the activity schedule;
6   clause 54.2 – revision of activity schedule;
7   clause 54.3 – reasons for not accepting the activity schedule.

Clause 11.2(20) – definition of activity schedule

This is a clause new to NEC3. It states simply that the 'activity schedule' (as a defined term) is the activity schedule identified in the contract data unless later changed in accordance with the contract. Its purpose is to allow the phrase 'activity schedule' to be used as a defined term in other clauses of the contract. And when so used it is then the current activity schedule which is referred to.

Clause 11.2(22) – definition of defined cost

Defined cost for options A and B is defined by:

1   the shorter schedule of cost components;
2   whether the work is subcontracted or not;
3   excluding the cost of preparing quotations for compensation events.

The first part of the clause restricts recovery on cost basis to the items detailed in the shorter schedule of cost components. The second part of the clause referring to subcontracted work highlights a point which is not too obvious from the schedules of cost components. This is that for options A and B the contractor cannot simply put forward subcontract invoices as evidence of defined cost. Subcontractor costs are to be calculated with reference to the rules of the shorter schedule of cost components in the same manner as the contractor's costs. However, under NEC3, the contract data does provide for a separate fee percentage to be applied to subcontractor costs.

The final part of clause 11.2(22) states that defined cost excludes the cost of preparing quotations for compensation events. This is a surprising provision to find in NEC3 which is promoted as being a fair contract. Since many compensation events arise from defaults for which the employer is responsible, the contractor should be able to recover the costs he incurs. This is particularly so where the contractor is instructed to prepare quotations or alternative quotations for proposed changes which are not later instructed.

Under NEC2 the corresponding provision generated much resentment amongst contractors and considerable ingenuity went into efforts to recover the costs of preparing quotations for compensation events. In some cases these costs ran into huge sums. One interesting line of argument was to the effect that it could be implied from the provision that compensation events would be few and far between and where there were multiple compensation events there was breach and the costs of preparing quotations were recoverable under clause 60.1(18) – the compensation event for breach of contract.

Clause 11.2(27) – definition of price for work done to date

The defined term 'the price for work done to date' governs the amount the contractor is due to be paid (clause 50.2) at both interim and final stages. The definition for the price for work done to date is the total of the prices:

1 for each group of completed activities; and
2 each completed activity which is not in a group; and
3 which is without defects which would delay following work or which would be covered immediately by following work.

It is usually up to the contractor how he forms his activity schedule and whether or not he shows grouping of activities. The contractor has to keep in mind that only completed groups of activities, or completed single activities, attract entitlement to interim payment. There is no contractual advantage to the contractor in grouping activities together but the disadvantage is obvious enough. For example, rather than describing 'painting' as one activity, the contractor would be well advised to split this trade into the separate activities of base coat, top coat and touching up.

The reference to defects in the price for work done to date is worded so as to permit a certain level of defects to be tolerated without prejudicing the contractor's right to payment.

Note that activities which are not included in the activity schedule do not come within the scope of the definition of 'prices' in clause 11.2(30) and therefore are not within the scope of 'the price for work done to date' in clause 11.2(27). Consequently omitted activities never attract a separate right to payment and are deemed to be covered in the listed activities.

Clause 11.2(30) – definition of the prices

The prices are defined as the lump sum prices for each of the activities in the activity schedule unless changed later in accordance with the contract.

The phrase 'unless changed later' ensures that the definition of the prices remains valid from tender to completion. But note that the changes are to be 'in accordance with the contract' and they do not extend to other changes of the lump sum price or prices which may be agreed between the parties.

Clause 54.1 – The activity schedule

The purpose of clause 54.1, which states only that information in the activity schedule is not works information or site information, is apparently to ensure that the activity schedule is restricted to a pricing document and does not acquire unintended contractual effect in respect of the works to be done.

For general comment on the activity schedule see Chapter 2.

Clause 54.2 – revision of activity schedule

In order to maintain the integrity of the payment system for option A, which relies on the identification of the completed activities and the integrity of the scheme for assessment of compensation events, NEC3 requires compatibility between the activity schedule and the accepted programme.

Clause 54.2 requires the contractor to submit a revised activity schedule to the project manager for acceptance:

1   when he changes a planned method of working;
2   at his discretion; and
3   if as a consequence the activities on the activity schedule do not relate to operations on the accepted programme.

It is not wholly clear why clause 54.2 is confined to changes in working made at the contractor's 'discretion'. Changes imposed on the contractor by compensation events are just as likely to affect the activity schedule. Perhaps it is assumed that these changes are already incorporated into the accepted programme via the compensation event procedures.

Clause 54.3 – reasons for not accepting the activity schedule

Clause 54.3 states three reasons for the project manager not accepting a revision of the activity schedule:

1 the revision does not comply with the accepted programme;
2 the changed prices are not distributed reasonably between the prices; and
3 the total of the prices is changed.

This final reason stated here provides confirmation, if it is needed, that the total of the prices in the original activity schedule is the total contract price (subject, of course, to contractual adjustments).

The consequences of not accepting a revised activity schedule are to leave payments and compensation events to be valued in accordance with the previous activity schedule.

Clause 10.6 – payments – main option B

The core clauses particular to main option B – the priced contract with bill of quantities – are:

1 clause 11.2(21) – definition of bill of quantities;
2 clause 11.2(22) – definition of defined cost;
3 clause 11.2(28) – definition of the price for work done to date;
4 clause 11.2(31) – definition of the prices.

Clause 11.2(21) – definition of bill of quantities

This is another clause new to NEC3. It states that the 'bill of quantities' (as a defined term) is the bill of quantities identified in the contract data as changed to accommodate implemented compensation events and accepted quotations for acceleration. Its purpose is similar to that of clause 11.2(20) found in option A – namely to allow the phrase 'bill of quantities' to be used as a defined term in other clauses of the contract. However, it is not entirely clear why its wording differs from that of clause 11.2(20) in referring to compensation events and acceleration.

Clause 11.2(22) – definition of defined cost

This is the same clause as used for option A – for comment see clause 10.5 above.

Clause 11.2(28) – definition of the price for work done to date

The price for work done to date is stated in clause 11.2(28) as:

1 the quantity of completed work for each bill of quantities item multiplied by the appropriate rate; and
2 such proportion of each lump sum in the bill of quantities as is completed.

The clause states further that completed work means work without defects which would either delay or be covered by immediately following work.

Clause 11.2(31) – definition of the prices

The prices are defined as: the lump sums, and the amounts obtained by multiplying the rates by the quantities for the items in the bill of quantities unless changed in accordance with the contract.

NEC3 defines prices so that a rate multiplied by a quantity is regarded as a price.

Clause 10.7 – payments – main option C

The following payments core clauses are particular to main option C – the target contract with activity schedule:

1 clause 11.2(20) – definition of activity schedule;
2 clause 11.2(23) – definition of defined cost;
3 clause 11.2(25) – definition of disallowed cost;
4 clause 11.2(29) – definition of the price for work done to date;
5 clause 11.2(30) – definition of the prices;
6 clause 50.6 – assessing the amount due;
7 clauses 52.2 and 52.3 – records of defined cost;
8 clauses 53.1 to 53.4 – the contractor's share;
9 clauses 54.1 to 54.3 – the activity schedule.

Clause 11.2(20) – definition of activity schedule

This is the same clause as found in option A – for comment see clause 10.5 above.

Clause 11.2(23) – definition of defined cost

In NEC2 'actual cost' was defined fairly simply as amounts due to subcontractors for work which was subcontracted, plus the costs of components in the schedules of cost components for work not subcontracted, less disallowed costs. The definition in clause 11.2(23) of NEC3 of the replacement term 'defined cost' is less concise because of the inclusion of a list of five items, all deductions which the contractor may have made against subcontractors, which need not be taken into account in totalling the amounts due to subcontractors. These are:

1 retentions;
2 payments to the employer for failures to meet key dates;
3 correction of defects after completion;
4 payments to others; and
5 supply of equipment, etc. included in the charge for overhead costs.

The reason for the inclusion of these items in the clause is stated in the guidance notes to NEC3 to avoid double deduction from the contractor's account. It appears that some project managers under NEC2 interpreted 'amounts due to subcontractors' too literally. But apart from the new list of non-qualifying deductions, defined cost under NEC3 is the same as actual cost under NEC2 in being subcontractor costs plus direct costs less disallowed costs.

An interesting point of note is that whereas defined cost under clause 11.2(22) which applies to options A and B expressly excludes the costs of preparing quotations for compensation events, clause 11.2(23) which applies to options C, D and E has no such exclusion. It can reasonably be taken therefore that the costs of preparing quotations under these options are valid elements of defined cost.

The major difference between clauses 11.2(23) and 11.2(22), however, is that subcontractors' invoices can form part of defined cost under clause 11.2(23). Another significant difference is that the definition of defined cost under clause 11.2(23) expressly excludes disallowed costs. This difference results from the respective uses of defined cost under options A and C. Under option A defined cost is considered only in the assessment of compensation events – questions of disallowed cost should therefore not arise. Under option C the price for the work done to date is based on defined cost. Therefore, that which is not chargeable to the employer needs to be excluded.

Clause 11.2(25) – definition of disallowed cost

Disallowed costs under clause 11.2(25) of NEC3 are essentially the same as those under NEC2 but there are a few points of difference:

1 Clause 11.2(25) does not include as a disallowed cost the cost of paying a subcontractor more for a compensation event than included in a quotation or assessment. Although, on its face, it seems reasonable that this should be disallowed, and that no doubt was why it was included in NEC2, the reality is that under options C, D and E to which clause 11.2(25) applies the contractor is obliged to pay the subcontractor on a cost basis if the subcontract is also under option C, D or E.
2 Clause 11.2(25) adds 'supplier' to 'subcontractor' for costs which should not have been paid.
3 Clause 11.2(25) qualifies plant and materials not used with 'unless resulting from a change to the works information'.
4 Clause 11.2(25) adds as a new item of disallowed cost 'preparation for and conduct of an adjudication or proceedings of the tribunal'.
5 Clause 11.2(25) changes correcting defects caused by the contractor not complying with a 'requirement' in the works information to not complying with a 'constraint' in the works information.

The full list of items of disallowed cost in clause 11.2(25) is as follows:

1 costs not justified by accounts and records;
2 costs which should not have been paid to subcontractors or suppliers;
3 costs incurred because the contractor did not follow an acceptance or procurement procedure in the works information or did not give an early warning;
4 costs of correcting defects after completion;
5 costs of correcting defects caused by not complying with a constraint in the works information;
6 plant and materials not used to provide the works – after allowing for reasonable wastage and unless resulting from a change in the works information;

7   resources not used to provide the works or not taken away when requested; and
8   preparation for and conduct of adjudication or tribunal proceedings.

Most of these are straightforward in principle even if open to argument on their application in particular circumstances. However, what may cause some surprise is that the costs of correcting defects before completion are apparently not disallowed unless the defects are caused by the contractor not complying with a constraint in the works information. Thus, amongst other things, defects caused by the contractor's design can apparently be corrected at cost – which raises questions on the suitability of using option C (and other cost reimbursable options) with the contractor's design.

Clause 11.2(29) – definition of the price for work done to date

This clause states that the price for work done to date is the defined cost which the project manager forecasts will have been paid by the contractor before the next assessment date plus the fee.

Clause 11.2(30) – definition of the prices

This is the same clause as for option A – for general comment see clause 10.5. However, it is important to note that the prices have far less contractual importance in option C than in option A. In particular in option A the prices form the foundation of the price for work done to date (which governs the final contract price) whereas in option C the prices play no part in the price for work done to date and only affect the final contract price through calculations of the contractor's share (clause 53).

Clause 50.6 – assessing the amount due

Clause 50.6 deals with the situation when payments for actual cost are made by the contractor in a currency other than the currency of the contract.

The clause provides that in such circumstances the amount due to the contractor is calculated by reference to the currency of the cost but for calculation of the fee and the contractor's share payments are converted to the currency of the contract.

Clause 52.2 – records of defined cost

In keeping with the cost reimbursable aspect of option C clause 52.2 requires the contractor to keep records of his defined cost including, and expressly:

1   accounts of payments of defined cost;
2   records showing repayments made;
3   records relating to compensation events for subcontractors; and
4   other records and accounts as stated in the works information.

Clause 52.3 – inspection of records

Clause 52.3 provides that the contractor shall allow the project manager to inspect the records at any time within working hours. Since it is the project manager's obligation to assess amounts due to the contractor this is clearly an essential provision.

Clauses 53.1 to 53.4 – the contractor's share

For any contractor considering entering into a target cost contract one of the key questions is: what are the potential risks and rewards arising from excesses or savings on the target cost? For general comment on this see Chapter 2.

Some target cost contracts have very simple formulae for fixing the contractor's and employer's shares of excesses and savings. NEC3 has an incremental scheme generally the same as that in NEC2 which requires the employer to state in the contract data (the percentage terms) ranges of deviation from the target cost and corresponding share percentages.

Clause 53.1 – calculating the share

Clause 53.1 of NEC2 was commonly regarded as a masterpiece of obfuscation. It remains unchanged in NEC3. The guidance notes to NEC3 helpfully provide, at page 66, a worked example of how the clause is to be understood.

Clause 53.2 – payment of the share

This clause appears to do little more than state the obvious – namely, that the contractor is paid his share of any saving and that he pays his share of any excess. But this clause may be necessary since in the event of excess the contractor will have been overpaid under the rules of NEC3 and the obligation to repay his share of the excess needs to be clearly stated.

Clause 53.3 – preliminary assessment of the share

Clause 53.3 requires the project manager to make a preliminary assessment of the contractor's share at completion of the whole of the works. The assessment is made using the project manager's forecasts for the final price for the work done to date and the final prices (which are the tender prices adjusted for compensation events and the like). This share is to be included in the amount due 'following' completion of the whole of the works. This probably means that the contractor's share included in the assessment made 'at' completion under clause 50.1.

Note that as NEC3 does not provide for interim assessments of the contractor's share before completion the contractor is fully reimbursed on a cost basis up to completion. In this respect the NEC3 is significantly different from target contracts of the type where the target mechanism operates in part as a guaranteed maximum price and where payment cuts off when this is reached.

Clause 53.4 – final assessment of the share

The final assessment of the share is made using the final price for work done to date and the final total of the prices. This share is included in the final amount due – so, unless there are complications, it should be included in the amount certified after the issue of the defects certificate.

Proposals for reducing defined cost

Missing from the NEC3 is a clause corresponding to clause 53.5 of NEC2 which provided that if the project manager accepted a proposal by the contractor to change the works information so as to reduce actual costs, the prices were not reduced. This allowed the contractor to keep any benefit by way of increased share.

Clauses 54.1 to 54.3 – the activity schedule

In option C, the activity schedule serves a different purpose than in option A. Whereas in option A the activity schedule is used to assess interim payments, in option C the activity schedule is used only in the assessment of compensation events and in detailing the total of the prices for calculation of the contractor's share.

Clauses 54.1 to 54.3 are the same clauses as used in option A – see clause 10.5 for comment.

Clause 10.8 – payments – main option D

The payment core clauses particular to main option D – the target contract with bill of quantities – are:

1 clause 11.2(21) – definition of bill of quantities;
2 clause 11.2(23) – definition of defined cost;
3 clause 11.2(25) – definition of disallowed cost;
4 clause 11.2(29) – definition of the price for work done to date;
5 clause 11.2(31) – definition of the prices;
6 clause 11.2(33) – definition of 'the total of the prices';
7 clause 50.6 – assessing the amount due;
8 clauses 53.2 and 53.3 – records of actual cost;
9 clauses 53.5 to 53.8 – the contractor's share.

Clauses 11.2(21) and 11.2(31) are common to options B and D. For comment see clause 10.6. Clauses 11.2(23), (25), (29), 50.6 and 52.3 are common to options C and D – for comment see the previous section.

Clause 11.2(33) is a definition used solely in option D. It introduces as a defined term 'the total of the prices', and describes this as:

1 the quantity of work completed for each item in the bill of quantities multiplied by the rate; and
2 a proportion of each lump sum proportioned to the completed work covered by the item.

This is in fact the definition of the price for work done to date found in clause 11.2(28) of option B and the sole purpose of repeating it in option D under a new number seems to be to facilitate expressions of, and perhaps calculation of, the contractor's share. So much can be gathered from the renumbering of clauses 53.1 to 53.4 in option C as clauses 53.5 to 53.8 in option D and the replacement of the phrase 'the total of the Prices' in option C with the phrase 'the Total of the Prices' in option D.

Note that bill of quantities in option D serves the same purpose as the activity schedule in option C and is not used for assessing interim payments.

Clause 10.9 – payments – main option E

The following payment core clauses are particular to main option E – the cost reimbursable contract:

1 clause 11.2(23) – definition of defined cost;
2 clause 11.2(25) – definition of disallowed cost;
3 clause 11.2(29) – definition of the price for work done to date;
4 clause 11.2(32) – definition of the prices;
5 clause 50.7 – assessing the amount due;
6 clause 52.2 and 52.3 – records of actual cost.

Because main option E is a fully cost reimbursable contract it does not include clauses relating to the contractor's share or to either an activity schedule or a bill of quantities. Accordingly, no further comment is required here. Clauses 11.2(23), (25), (29), 52.2 and 52.3, which are common to options C and D, have been considered earlier.

Clause 11.2(32) – definition of the prices

The prices are defined simply as the defined cost plus the fee.

There is no significance in the use of the term 'prices' as opposed to 'price'. It seems to be used simply to achieve compatibility with other clauses of the contract.

Clause 50.7 – assessing the amount due

This clause is similar to clause 50.6 used in options C and D for dealing with payments made by the contractor in currencies other than the currency of the contract except that it omits the reference in clause 50.6 to the contractor's share.

Clause 10.10 – payments – main option F

The payment core clauses particular to main option F – the management contract – are:

1 clause 11.2(24) – definition of defined cost;
2 clause 11.2(26) – definition of disallowed costs;
3 clause 11.2(29) – definition of the price for work done to date;
4 clause 11.2(32) – definition of the prices;
5 clause 50.7 – assessing the amount due;
6 clauses 52.2 and 52.3 – records of defined cost.

From the above list only clauses 11.2(24) and (26) differ from the clauses also applicable to main option E.

Clause 11.2(24) – definition of defined cost

The difference between the definition of defined cost in clause 11.2(24) and the definition found in clause 11.2(23) which applies to options C, D and E is that for work done by the contractor himself; clause 11.2(24) refers to 'the prices', whereas clause 11.2(23) refers to the costs of components in the schedule of costs components.

Clause 11.2(26) – definition of disallowed cost

The differences between the definition in clause 11.2(26) of disallowed cost and the definition in clause 11.2(25) applicable to options C, D and E are firstly that clause 11.2(26) omits the reference in clause 11.2(25) to:

1 the costs of correcting defects;
2 the costs of plant and materials not used to provide the works; and
3 the costs of resources not used to provide the works or not taken away when requested.

This suggests that there is less disallowed cost under option F than under the other cost reimbursable options, but that is not intended to be the case.

Normally all the work in option F will be subcontracted on NEC terms as packages on lump sum prices and each subcontractor will be responsible for correcting his own defects at his own cost. Only if the contractor does some of the work himself will the omitted items of disallowed costs be of any significance.

Other differences are:

1   clause 11.2(26) does not include as disallowed cost preparation for and conduct of adjudication and tribunal proceedings;
2   clause 11.2(26) includes as disallowed cost payment to a subcontractor for work which the contract data states the contractor will do himself or payment to a subcontractor for the contractor's management.

Frequently asked questions

Q. Under NEC main option A is the contractor entitled to be paid a percentage for part completed activities?

A. No. Under NEC main option A the price for work done to date only includes completed activities. No value for an activity is included until that activity is completed. A completed activity is one which is without defects which would either delay or be covered by immediately following works.

Q. Under NEC main option C is the contractor entitled to include within his defined cost lump sum prices provided by subcontractors?

A. Yes. Under NEC main option C the definition of defined cost includes the amount of payments due to subcontractors. This is to be contrasted with main option A where the definition of defined cost is the cost of components in the shorter schedule of cost components whether work is subcontracted or not.

5

Payment notices

Types of notices

In any construction project, communication between all parties
is very important. It allows all parties to manage unforeseen
circumstances and optimise project cost, completion time and
the use of resources. The communication of problems can
impact upon responsibility for problems and ensuing
entitlements. Most of the standard form construction contracts
have developed a formalised system of 'notices'. These notices
ensure that critical communications are made according to
strict timescales, and that failure to observe these requirements
has implications for liabilities and entitlements.

This chapter discusses the meaning and ramifications of
contractor's delay notices. The subject of employer's withholding
notices under HGCRA 1996 is covered in Chapter 8 below.

Delay management

Many construction contracts allow the contractor to apply for
an extension of time where certain conditions are met. Often, a
'relevant event' (sometimes a 'compensation event') will trigger
the right. These 'events' are usually events beyond the
contractor's control (e.g. strikes, inclement weather or delays
caused by the employer or architect) for which risk the parties
have agreed a compensation mechanism in advance in the
contract.

It is important that 'events' are communicated up the contract
chain. This is achieved by means of a notice. If the contractor
does not serve a notice in some cases he will be wholly
disentitled to an extension of time in relation to a 'relevant
event', and may perhaps be liable for liquidated damages for
the unauthorised delay. Each contract deals with notice

requirements slightly differently. Provided below is an outline of the mechanisms in FIDIC, IChemE, JCT and NEC3 contracts.

The FIDIC position

The FIDIC position is typical of many standard form construction contracts. The contractor's notice of delay is a condition precedent to an extension of time, but there is no penalty attached to an employer's failure to respond to the contractor's application. Clause 20.1 of FIDIC is a complex provision with a series of different layers and ought to be considered with care:

> 'If the Contractor considers himself entitled to any extension of the Time for Completion and/or any additional payment . . . the Contractor shall give notice to the Employer, describing the event or circumstances giving rise to the claim . . . as soon as practicable, and not later than 28 days after the Contractor became aware, or should have become aware, of the event or circumstance.

> If the Contractor fails to give notice of a claim within such period of 28 days, the Time for Completion shall not be extended, the Contractor shall not be entitled to additional payment, and the Employer shall be discharged from all liability in connection with the claim.

> Within 42 days after receiving a claim or any further particulars supporting a previous claim, or within such period as may be proposed by the Employer and approved by the Contractor, the Employer shall respond with approval, or with disapproval and detailed comments. He may also request, as soon as reasonably possible, any necessary further particulars, but shall nevertheless give his response on the principles of the claim within such time.'

The IChemE position

The IChemE Standard Form adopts a similar position to FIDIC. Clause 14.1 of the IChemE Standard Form of Contract (Lump Sum, *The Red Book*, 4th edition, 2001) states:

'If the Contractor is delayed in the performance of any of his obligations under the Contract by any of the [relevant events, he] . . . shall forthwith give notice to the Project Manager.

The Contractor shall advise the Project Manager of the extension of any date or period specified in the Contract for the completion of such obligations which he considers would be fair and reasonable in the circumstances. The Contractor shall keep contemporaneous records of the circumstances, extent and effect of such delay. The Project Manager shall, within fourteen days of the time that the extent and consequences of any such delay are known, issue a Variation Order both to the Purchaser and to the Contractor stating the appropriate extension to the Approved Programme and to Schedule 11 (Times of completion) . . .'

The JCT position

The JCT contract requires the contractor to provide a notice where delay is anticipated or occurring. Responsibility then falls to the architect/contract administrator to extend the completion date where he considers it reasonable to do so. The JCT Standard Form of Building Contract ('Private With Quantities', 2005) states:

'Clause 2.27 ("Notice by Contractor of Delay to Progress")

If and whenever it becomes reasonably apparent that the Progress of the Works or any Section is being or is likely to be delayed the Contractor shall forthwith give written notice to the Architect/Contract Administrator of the material circumstances, including the cause or causes of the delay, and shall identify in the notice any event which in his opinion is a Relevant Event.

Clause 2.28 ("Fixed Completion Date")

If, in the opinion of the Architect/Contract Administrator, on receiving a notice and particulars under clause 2.27: (1) any of the events which are stated to be a cause of delay is a Relevant Event; and (2) completion of the Works or of any Section is likely to be delayed thereby beyond the relevant Completion Date, then, save where these Conditions expressly provide otherwise, the Architect/Contract Administrator shall give an extension of time by fixing such later date as the Completion Date for the Works or Section as he then estimates to be fair and reasonable.'

Note, however, under the JCT provisions the architect (in the Standard Form, Clause 2.28.5) or the employer (in, e.g., the Design and Build) has an obligation at the end of the project to reconsider and deal finally with the question of extensions of time within a period of 12 weeks. This must be fair and reasonable in light of all the circumstances, irrespective of any notification by the contractor. Moreover, save in relation to omissions, it can only increase the extension of time. Whilst, therefore, the provision of a notice may well be a condition precedent for the granting of an extension during the course of the works, it is not a condition precedent for being granted an extension after practical completion.

The NEC3 position

The NEC3 contract establishes a mechanism to force both parties to correspond and co-operate with each other before, during and after delays occur. Clause 61.3 was added to the latest 2005 edition of the Engineering and Construction Contract to make a notice of delay a condition precedent to any variation in the price or completion date, and also to impose an eight-week 'time bar' on any notices. Additional provisions act on the project manager to combat a tendency to ignore contractors' notices and fail to respond efficiently to possible delays.

The NEC3 Standard Form Contract 2005 Edition (Option B: Priced Contract with Bill of Quantities) provides that:

'Clause 16 ("Early Warning")

The Contractor and the Project Manager give an early warning by notifying the other as soon as either becomes aware of any matter which could . . . delay Completion.

Clause 61 ("Notifying Compensation Events")

The Contractor notifies the Project Manager of an event which has happened or which he expects to happen as a compensation event if the Contractor believes that the event is a compensation event and the Project Manager has not notified the event to the Contractor.

If the Contractor does not notify a compensation event within eight weeks of becoming aware of the event, he is not entitled to a change in the Prices, the Completion Date or a Key Date unless the Project Manager should have notified the event to the Contractor but did not . . . If the Project Manager does not notify his decision to the Contractor within either (1) one week of the Contractor's notification; or (2) a longer period to which the Contractor has agreed, the Contractor may notify the Project Manager to this effect. A failure by the Project Manager to reply within two weeks of this notification is treated as acceptance by the Project Manager that the event is a compensation event and an instruction to submit quotations.'

In practice, evidence from the industry suggests that the NEC3 mechanism goes too far and creates new problems. Contractors have taken to bombarding project managers with notices for every possible minor delay in the knowledge that a failure to respond provides them with an extension by default. Parties often agree midway through the project to suspend this mechanism and instead opt for periodic schedules of delay or regular project negotiations.

The following cases are indicative of the courts' approach to notices for extensions of time.

Merton LBC v Stanley Hugh Leach Ltd [1985] 32 BLR 51

A contract based on the JCT Standard Form 1963 Edition required the contractor to notify the architect 'upon it becoming reasonably apparent that the progress of the Works is delayed'. The contractor was slow to serve the delay notice.

Vinelott J held that, while a timely notice was not a condition precedent to an extension of time (under the 1963 Edition), the contractor could not rely on his own delay to gain a greater extension than that to which he would otherwise have been entitled.

Turner Corporation Ltd (Receiver and Manager Appointed) v Austotel Pty Ltd [1997] 13 BCL 378

A contractor was already in significant delay; the architect was five months late in issuing instructions regarding the provision of a gas leak detector. The contractor failed at the time to request an extension of time, but later sought to rely on the architect's lateness as an act of prevention. The Australian Court held that the contractor could not rely upon the prevention principle (see below) where it had failed to exercise a contractual right which would have negated the effect of that preventing conduct with an extension of time.

Gaymark Investments Pty Ltd v Walter Construction Group Ltd [1999] NTSC 143

A contract for the construction of a hotel in Darwin was based on an Australian standard form building contract. The provision which would have entitled the contractor to an extension of time, where it had not served a notice, had been deleted thereby making the notice a condition precedent. Delay was caused by the employer; the contractor did not serve a delay notice. The Supreme Court of the Northern Territory of Australia agreed with the arbitrator's determination that even though the contractor had not served a delay notice, the delay constituted an act of prevention. It concluded that there was no date for practical completion and time was put at large.

City Inn Ltd v Shepherd Construction Ltd [2003] SLT 885

Shepherd was contracted to construct a hotel in Bristol. The works were delayed as a result of the employer's action, and Shepherd was awarded a four-week extension of time (extended to five weeks at adjudication). The employer sued for liquidated damages for delay, arguing that Shepherd had not strictly complied with the formal notice requirements. The Second Division of the Scottish Inner House allowed the employer's claim, reasoning that where a party has agreed to specific formal requirements, it should be obliged to follow them.

Multiplex Constructions (UK) Ltd v Honeywell Control Systems Ltd (No. 2) [2007] EWHC 447

Honeywell was engaged as a subcontractor by Multiplex for works in connection with the new Wembley National Stadium. The works were already in delay before Honeywell began.

During the course of the works, Multiplex issued three revised programmes, none of which were completed on time. Honeywell failed to provide adequate delay notices (as required under the contract) but nonetheless claimed extensions of time because Multiplex's programme revisions: (a) set time at large; or (b) rendered the notice mechanism inoperable; or (c) in any case, following *Gaymark*, Honeywell should be entitled to an extension of time. Jackson J held that:

1   acts of prevention do not set time at large where there is an adequate extension of time mechanism;
2   acts of prevention do not render notice mechanisms inoperable; it fell to Honeywell to do all it reasonably could to provide notices and supporting information; and
3   although distinguishing *Gaymark* on other grounds, he held obiter that *Gaymark* was unlikely to represent English law as regards notice provisions, because it would benefit any contractor to 'disregard with impunity any provision making proper notice a condition precedent'.

The 'prevention principle' and 'time at large'

The courts have developed the 'prevention principle' in relation to applications for extensions of time. In sum, this principle prevents the employer from refusing to grant an extension of time, and subsequently benefiting from liquidated damages for delay, in circumstances where the employer himself was the cause of the delay.

The following cases illustrate the development and operation of the prevention principle.

Holme v Guppy (1838) 150 ER 1195

Completion of a construction project was delayed by some four-and-a-half weeks, four weeks of which were due to the employer failing to deliver access to the site. The employer sued for liquidated damages. The Court of Exchequer, establishing the 'prevention principle', held that:

> '... if the party be prevented by the refusal of the other contracting party from completing the contract within the time limited he is not liable in law for the default ... the plaintiffs were therefore left at large. Consequently they are not to forfeit anything for the delay.'

Dodd v Churton [1897] 1 QB 562

A contractor was delayed in completing a construction project because the architect had issued additional instructions. The Court of Appeal held that, although the employer was entitled to request additional works, he could not then claim liquidated damages for any associated delay to the original completion date.

Peak Construction (Liverpool) Ltd v McKinney Foundations Ltd (1971) 1 BLR 111

A construction contract empowered the architect to extend the completion date in 'unforeseen circumstances'. During the course of the works, certain piles were found to be defective. All work ceased for some 58 weeks, ostensibly while the employer decided the appropriate remedial solution. Remedial works then took six weeks. The employer claimed liquidated damages for the whole delay. The Court of Appeal dismissed the claim, reasoning that if any act of the employer prevents the contractor completing the works on time, they will forfeit any right to liquidated damages for delay unless they have expressly provided for this eventuality in their contract.

Frequently asked questions

Q. When the contract states that a notice must be issued by the contractor in the event of a claim for loss and expense or an extension of time does failure to issue that notice deprive the contractor of any entitlement?

A. Generally not, but it depends on the terms of the contract. For a notice requirement to be a condition precedent to an entitlement very clear words must be used. The contract must state clearly that issue of the notice is a condition precedent to entitlement or alternatively that the contractor will not receive any entitlement unless the notice has been issued. In the absence of such clear words the courts will generally interpret notice requirements as an administrative process. Failure to issue the notice is still a breach of contract for which damages may be claimed (provided that they can be proved) but the contractor will still be able to recover for the loss and expense or extension of time that should have formed the subject of the notice. Unless the contract states otherwise the courts will generally accept any form of communication as adequate notice. This may include a letter, a minute of a meeting or even a note of a telephone conversation.

6

Measurement and valuation in the JCT Contract

Introduction

Variations and related claims for additional payment or extension of time are to be expected on even the best-planned projects. Technical complexity, new technology, multi-organisational participation, and the inherent uncertainty in the physical, financial and economic environments in which projects have to be executed make the complete avoidance of such claims an unrealistic aim. All the major reports on sources of inefficiency in the construction industry identify variations and claims as major factors. Most contracts deal with this problem by providing a code for dealing with:

1   the scope of variations allowed;
2   the valuation of varied work;
3   assessment of payment for impact on other work; and
4   remedies for delays and disruption caused by variations.

The Joint Contract Tribunal's Standard Form of Building Contract, 1998 edition (JCT 98), contains easily the most extensive and complex code of any form of contract. However, in the 2005 edition, in common with the general themes of reform, valuation rules are simplified in terms of their complexity and language.

This chapter examines various contractual provisions on variations with the aim of providing guidance on practical implications and how to avoid or deal with potential pitfalls. In the absence of an express power to do so, there is no power for a contract administrator to vary the works. This would lead to situations where the employer, through the contract administrator could not alter or omit works and could only have the original works built without change.

Any attempt to change the works would be outside the contract and would result in a series of collateral contracts which would be unnecessarily complicated and create an unacceptable degree of uncertainty.

In view of this, the draft of the standard forms of construction contract provide mechanisms of varying complexity to enable the contract administrator to vary the works under the contract and a series of rules governing how such changes are to be valued.

General provisions for variation

The courts may well adopt a compromise and interpret the contract in such a way that the contractor is compelled to comply with instructions to provide additional works, but see fit to interpret the rules of valuation in a liberal fashion. However, the power of the supervising officer to instruct additional works may well only apply in so far as it is still within the context of the contract that has been entered into; for example, if the supervising officer amended the layout of the partition wall and in doing so increased the quantity then that is an addition which is acceptable. However, if the supervising officer sees a particularly attractive rate against an item of fencing between properties, he cannot, it is submitted, take further advantage of this rate by issuing an instruction to fence a field remote from the site. However, the extent to which he could require additional fencing within the site is arguable and will be further discussed below in connection with bad rates.

Regrettably, the omission of work by way of a variation instruction can cause similar problems of interpretation and in some instances give greater problems. The clause used in JCT contracts again appears to put no restriction on the extent of work that may be omitted, so in stark contrast to a contract not providing for variations and where therefore no work can be omitted (unless by separate agreement) JCT contracts apparently provide for the total omission of work.

The concern of the contractor is whether in omitting work he will: (i) lose an element of his profit; (ii) lose a disproportionate amount of overheads and profit; and (iii) be paid any additional costs for performing the lesser amount of the work. Presumably, if he can satisfy himself that he will not lose out on any of these items then he will readily accede to the variation. Frequently, however, he is not so satisfied and one is left endeavouring to establish the position in respect of omitted work.

It has been said in *Gallagher v Hirsch* (1899) that the word 'omission' only contemplated things to be left out of the contract altogether, not such as were taken out of the contract and given to another. This therefore puts a severe restriction on the supervising officer in that it must be the intention not to have any of the work omitted executed by others. A number of questions come to mind:

1   Is the contractor bound by any rules of valuation in respect of the omitted work and the work that is now left?
2   Can the supervising officer omit all the work if he genuinely desires the work not to proceed?
3   What is the significance if the work is omitted and given to others?
4   How does the contractor know it is not the intention of the client to get the work executed by others?

Broadly, the answer is that the contractor is bound by the rules of valuation in respect of omitted work where the omission is a genuine omission of work, and he may therefore lose an element of his profit. The contractor may also be bound by the rules of valuation in respect of omitted work which is given to others but would be able to sue for damages for breach of contract. The pursuit of damages in law for such a breach of contract is easily avoided by ensuring that the contractor does not lose out financially because of the omission of work by recognising his entitlement to loss of profit and providing for it in the valuation. Either way the client will suffer cost on account of omitting the work but probably to a lesser extent by following this course of action rather than litigation.

Valuation of variations

The first step in the process of valuing variations is to establish whether an architect's instruction constitutes a variation as defined by the conditions of contract that have been adopted. Clearly, if an architect's instruction does not constitute a variation then no evaluation under the rules of valuation should take place. This seems self evident but it is surprising how frequently quantity surveyors, architects and engineers value instructions for the purpose of establishing an interim advance or indeed the final account figure which are not variations or otherwise provided for in the contract. Where this occurs it is generally at the initiation of the contractor for he sees all instructions as having financial effect. Therefore, on occasion, contractors will make claims in respect of such payment and these claims will be acceded to, because superficially the instruction seems to justify some financial recompense and the lack of time often restricts further investigation of the instructions.

Although an instruction may not be a variation by definition, it may still have cost consequences. For example, clause 8.3 of JCT 98 provides for an adjustment to the contract sum, on account of opening up and testing, unless this is provided for in the contract bills or the test shows defective work. Such testing and making good need not be valued under the rules of valuation for variations as it is not a variation. However, if a provisional sum is included to cover such work then it falls to be valued under the rules of valuation (JCT 98). Therefore if one establishes that the instruction does not constitute a variation one must look to establish whether any other clause of the contract provides for adjustment.

Having established that an instruction does constitute a valid variation, then it has to be valued in accordance with the rules of valuation (if any) contained within the contract conditions. Before looking at the way individual standard forms of contract deal with the valuation of variations it is worth detailing in general terms the various means which can be adopted.

Lump sum quotations

The contractor may give a lump sum quotation in respect of the variation in advance of performing it, for acceptance by the employer or his agents. This approach has the advantage of simplicity and allows the parties to the contract to know exactly where they stand financially before the work is executed. The lump sum quotation may include all aspects of the variation: for example, the variation itself, other work affected and the costs resulting from any delays or disruption the variation may produce.

Unfortunately, such simplicity is no panacea for it suffers the following disadvantages:

1   The contractor is in a very strong position to secure recompense in excess of the true cost plus reasonable profit of the variation. This is so even where the amount is to be agreed by both parties.
2   The contractor may find he is unable accurately to value either the cost of the variation or its effect upon the project in advance of the execution of the work.

It is agreed that the latter of these is not really a disadvantage in that the contractor is expected to price the whole project in advance and therefore this is not in essence any different. However, it is submitted that there is a distinction between pricing an event where the contractor determines or is in a position to determine his action and having to accept the consequence of a change imposed upon him.

Cost reimbursement

Alternatively, the value of the variation may be based upon the actual cost, plus profit and overheads in respect of performing the work. Many contractors feel that this is the most equitable way of dealing with variations, but again it has its disadvantages:

1   It is difficult for such an approach to embrace the consequential effects of a variation without putting the client in an unenviable position unless strict monitoring and control of the contractor can be assured.
2   There is no real inducement or incentive for the contractor to perform efficiently.
3   Occasionally contractors may secure contracts on very favourable rates with the result that cost reimbursement can in these instances show an under recovery as far as the contractor is concerned.

The major problems with using bill rates, etc. are:

1   the tender may be subject to competition but the individual rates in themselves may not be competitive when used for a specific variation;

2 the individual rates may undervalue or overvalue the cost of an item and thus produce problems where a variation significantly increases or decreases the quantity of such items;

3 the variation items are frequently different or carried out under different circumstances from those in the contract documents, even though appearing similar;

4 it is dependent upon a high degree of personal opinion or judgment.

The problem referred to in 2 above can occur either because of an error in pricing or because of the deliberate action of the estimator. This action of the estimator is described as 'loading the rates' and can result in the contract rates being front loaded, back loaded or loaded in any other way thought desirable. The purpose of this exercise is twofold:

1 to improve or regulate cash flow; and
2 to improve recovery on anticipated variations.

There is nothing legally wrong in such practice but such manipulations can also work against the interests of the contractor. For example, he may assume certain work will be decreased in quantity therefore prices it at a lower rate, only to find that the quantity is increased substantially. Because such practices may distort the position, particularly with regard to the valuation of variations, one should take care in the evaluation of tenders to investigate this issue and to attempt to correct any imbalance of rates.

There are other issues which are also relevant and these are dealt with below in discussing the specific rules of variation which are frequently adopted.

Variations allowed under JCT SBC 2005

The extent of change to the parties' contractual obligations permitted under the contract is expressly set out in clause 5.1, which defines a 'variation' as follows:

'Definition of Variations

The term "Variation" means:

1   the alteration or modification of the design, quality or quantity of the Works including:
    (a) the addition, omission or substitution of any work;
    (b) the alteration of the kind or standard of any of the materials or goods to be used in the Works;
    (c) the removal from the site of any work executed or materials or goods brought thereon by the Contractor for the purposes of the Works other than work, materials or goods which are not in accordance with this Contract:
2   the imposition by the Employer of any obligations or restrictions in regard to the matters set out in this clause 5.1.2 or the addition to or alteration or omission of any such obligations or restrictions so imposed or imposed by the Employer in the Contract Bills or in the Employer's Requirements in regard to:
    (a) access to the site or use of any specific parts of the site;
    (b) limitation of working space;
    (c) limitations of working hours; or
    (d) the execution of completion of the work in any specific order.'

Clause 3.14 states that the architect may issue instructions requiring a variation. This can be done at any time before practical completion, including when the contractor is in culpable delay. In addition, clause 3.14 states that the architect may sanction in writing any change made by the contractor without an architect's instruction provided the change is within the definition of a 'variation'. Where valuation of the sanctioned variation would entail additional payment or delay, the architect would be well advised either to get express authority from the employer or sanction the change subject to appropriate conditions on entitlement to payment and extension of time.

Various clauses also provide that specified matters are to be dealt with as variations. For example, clause 2.14.1 –

corrections to departures from the applicable standard method of measurement; clause 2.17.2 – instructions to resolve conflicts between the Statutory Requirements and contractual documents; clauses B.3.5 and C.4.5.2 in Schedule 3 – work of restoration, replacement, or repair necessitated by damage by the risks covered by the clause 6.8 definition of 'All Risk Insurance'; clause 5.9 – other work affected by compliance with a variation or an architect's instructions as to the expenditure of a provisional sum, or execution of work for which an approximate quantity in the contract bills is different from the quantity actually required.

The general position is that, whilst work can be omitted (since the contract provides for it), work cannot be taken away from the contractor to be given to someone else (*Carr v JA Berriman Pty Ltd* (1953) 879 Con LR 327, *Amec Building Ltd v Cadmus Investment Co Ltd* (1996) 51 Con LR 105). Clause 13.1.3 of JCT 98 provides for a specific example of this by stating expressly that a variation does not include nomination of a subcontractor to do work priced as the contractor's work in the contract bills. The architect may, however, take work away from the contractor simply by omitting it if the work is not required.

It is to be noted that the clause 5.1 definition of a 'variation' is exhaustive. The contractor has no obligations to carry out an instruction purporting to be a variation, if the subject matter of the instruction falls outside the definition. An example of an invalid instruction would be one requiring the contractor to accelerate the works in order to finish before the applicable completion date because an acceleration order is not within the definition.

Challenging and objecting to variations

Clause 3.10.1 states that the contractor is not obliged to comply with a variation instruction under clause 3.14.1 to the extent that he makes reasonable objection to it in writing. The contract offers no clues as to what a reasonable objection may be. Differences as to whether an objection is reasonable are likely to involve the issue of whether the variation is within the ambit of the works as a whole. Any disagreements can be referred to an adjudicator in the first instance.

The general scheme for valuation of variations

Clause 5.2 directs that a variation instructed by the contract administrator is to be valued in accordance with clauses 5.6 to 5.10 (the 'valuation rules') unless it is to be agreed between the employer and the contractor or for which a Schedule 2 quotation has been confirmed as accepted. Alternative B applies to the extent that the alternative A procedure either is not initiated or otherwise fails to produce a price agreed to by the contractor and the quantity surveyor. There are therefore four methods for determining the price of a variation under the contract:

1 acceptance of Schedule 2 quotation;
2 agreement between the employer and contractor;
3 the valuation rules; and
4 any other method agreed between the employer and the contractor (hereafter 'collateral valuation agreement').

The 1998 suite of JCT Contracts provides for a further method known as the contractor's price statement (CPS). This was a method which allowed for the contractor to submit a statement based on the valuation rules setting out its proposed value of the variation. This was rarely used and invariably resulted in the architect or quantity surveyor applying the valuations rules himself. Given this, the JCT did not carry forward this procedure into the 2005 edition. However, the JCT 1998 remains in general use and as such the chapter will still address the CPS mechanism.

The operation of the alternatives is summarised below.

Alternative pricing by the contractor

Traditionally, the quantity surveyors had sole responsibility for pricing variations by the valuation rules method on behalf of the architect or contract administrator. However, contractors often contributed to the valuation process by providing their version of what the quantity surveyor should produce. The valuation so provided was vetted by the quantity surveyor and adopted, with or without adjustments, as his valuation. CPS alternative A is therefore nothing more than formalisation of this practice of contractors pricing variations in that the contractor is expected to produce a valuation in accordance with the basic method.

It is also to be noted that the CPS is not a quotation. It is not a vehicle for deciding whether work will or will not be done. It is simply a valuation of a variation instruction with which the contractor is obliged to comply. He has no choice in whether or not to do the work. Alternative A, however, gives him a chance to influence the valuation of the variation.

Within 21 days of receiving an instruction (or commencing the relevant work, where no instruction is involved, i.e. work for which an approximate quantity is included in the contract documents), the contractor may submit his price statement to the quantity surveyor. If there was insufficient information provided with the instruction to enable the contractor to prepare the statement, he may submit it within 21 days after receiving the necessary information. The contractor may also, if he wishes, attach to the price statement a separate statement of his requirements for extension of time and additional payment on account of disturbance to regular progress caused by the variation covered by the statement. This statement is hereafter referred to as an 'annexed claims statement'. The only proviso to his entitlement is that he must not request time or amounts which have already been awarded or ascertained under clauses 25 or 26 of JCT 98, or in an accepted clause 13A quotation. He may, however, duplicate requests made in other price statements or clause 13A quotations, which have not yet been accepted.

Dealing with the CPS

On receipt of a price statement, the quantity surveyor must consult with the architect, then write to the contractor (paragraph A2) within 21 days of receiving the statement, stating which of these is his decision:

1 the price statement is accepted;
2 the whole of the price statement is rejected; or
3 part of the price statement is not accepted.

If the CPS is accepted in whole or in part, the CPS or the accepted part of it becomes the amount of adjustment of the contract sum under clause 13.7 for the relevant part of the variation. If the CPS is not accepted, either in whole or in part, the quantity surveyor must write to the contractor giving reasons in similar detail to that in the CPS. He must also supply an amended price statement (APS) to the contractor.

Under paragraph A5, if the quantity surveyor fails to write to the contractor, the CPS is deemed rejected. It is provided expressly that the contractor may then refer the matter as a dispute to adjudication. This right to refer to adjudication seems to underline the importance of alternative A. It is a constant reminder to the quantity surveyor that he cannot ignore the contractor's submission, and also that he must act promptly and speedily in checking it within a tight timescale. Significantly, the right to refer to adjudication in paragraph A5 is limited to the contractor, whereas under s. 108 of HGCRA 1996 'either' party is entitled to refer any dispute or difference to adjudication at any time. Article 5 complies with the Act in this respect by stating that either party may at any time refer any dispute under the contract to adjudication. As a matter of construction, the employer may therefore also challenge the quantity surveyor's rejection, although this would be a very rare occurrence.

The contractor's response to the APS

Upon receipt of the quantity surveyor's APS, the contractor has 14 days to state that he accepts it all, or in part. There is no express requirement to do this in writing, although the prudent contractor would normally do this. To the extent that the contractor accepts the APS, the accepted amount becomes the relevant amount of adjustment of the contract sum in accordance with clause 13.7. If the contractor does not make a statement within the 14-day period, the contractor is deemed not to have accepted any part of the APS. At this point the submission of statements back and forth between the contractor and quantity surveyor ceases. To the extent that agreement has not been reached, either party may refer to adjudication the parts of the CPS and of the APS not agreed.

If, after following the alternative A procedures, neither the CPS nor the APS is accepted, and if the non-acceptance has not been referred to an adjudicator, paragraph A6 states that alternative B (implementation of the basic method by the quantity surveyor) applies. However, there is no timescale suggested and a dispute may arise when a quantity surveyor ignores his own APS in favour of a valuation under the basic method.

Dealing with an annexed claim statement

Claims for extra time and direct loss and/or expense are dealt with separately in paragraph A7. On receipt of a CPS with an annexed claims statement, the quantity surveyor must notify the contractor within 21 days either that the amount requested in lieu of loss and/or expense is, or is not, accepted. If not accepted, any loss and/or expense due will be ascertained by the architect under clause 26. The same applies to any request for extension of time. If not accepted, adjustment to the time for completion, if any, will be made by the architect under clause 25. It is arguable that an annexed claim statement can be accepted whilst the CPS itself is rejected.

There is no provision for the architect or the quantity surveyor to provide an amended response to an annexed claims statement. If the quantity surveyor does not respond within the 21-day period, clauses 25 and 26 apply as though the contractor had attached no time or loss and expense requirements to his price statement. Although the contractor may choose to submit details, there is no absolute obligation on the quantity surveyor to respond, neither is there any express remedy for the contractor. At common law, an assertion of entitlement that is not accepted by the other party amounts to a dispute and, as such, capable of being referred to adjudication (*Tradax Internacional SA v Cerrahogullaris TAS, The Eregli* [1981] Lloyd's Rep 169; *Ellerine Bros (Pty) Ltd v Klinger* [1982] L WLR 1375; *Hayter v Nelson* [1990] 8 Lloyd's Rep 265). It is, however, arguable that the absence of specific reference to adjudication implies that the matter cannot at this stage amount to a dispute under the contract. On this point, see *John Mowlem and Company v Hydra-Tight Ltd (t/a Hevilifts)* (2000) CILL 1649, in which the court adopted the parties' consensus that a contractual term stipulating that what is in effect a dispute in the ordinary sense is not a dispute before a preliminary procedure is exhausted contravenes the HGCRA 1996, thereby having the effect of importing the Scheme for Construction Contracts into the contract. However, as already explained, the effect of article 5 is that the contractor may refer the rejection at this point in time.

Alternative B: pricing by the quantity surveyor

As already explained, this involves the valuation by the quantity surveyor using the valuation rules.

Valuation via Schedule 2 quotation

The procedure for dealing with Schedule 2 quotations is as follows. If the architect wishes to deal with a variation under the quotation procedure, clause 5.3.1 requires him to state in the variation instruction that Schedule 2 shall apply. Such an instruction is essentially an invitation to the contractor to submit a quotation for the work entailed. Clause 5.3.1 further provides that the contractor may in writing, within seven days, decline the invitations. If the contractor so declines, then the architect must then revert to the ordinary variation instruction if he still requires the variation to be implemented. It is therefore to be noted that the quotation procedure is not mandatory. On the one hand, the architect may use it selectively whilst, on the other hand, the contractor may reject its use without any reasons, although most contractors would probably see the procedure as a potential benefit in principle.

The contract anticipates only three possible outcomes to an instruction that a variation is to be treated under the Schedule 2 quotation method. First, the contractor may reject it within the seven days. Secondly, if not rejected, the contractor may request further information within the seven days after which he must submit the quotation within 21 days of receipt of sufficient information. Thirdly, where none of the above applies, he must submit a quotation within 21 days of the initial instruction. These time limits can be adjusted by agreement although it is not specified whether it is to be with the architect or the employer.

The contractor's Schedule 2 quotation is submitted to the quantity surveyor (not the architect) and remains open for acceptance by the employer (not the quantity surveyor or the architect) for seven days after receipt of the quotation by the quantity surveyor. The content of the quotation is prescribed in Schedule 2. It must show the following information separately:

1   the value of adjustment to the contract sum (including loss and/or expense) determined in accordance with rates and prices in the contract bills;
2   the contractor's requirement for any adjustment to the completion date including if relevant, an earlier date than that stated in the appendix;
3   the fair amount to be paid in lieu of loss and/or expense;
4   a fair and reasonable amount in respect of preparing the Schedule 2 quotation;

5   a statement of any additional resources required to carry out the variation, if the Schedule 2 instruction specifically requires it; and

6   a method statement for carrying out the variation, if the Schedule 2 instruction specifically requires it.

Acceptance/rejection of the quotation

Acceptance of the quotation

It is the employer who makes it known to the contractor under Schedule 2 that he wishes to accept the Schedule 2 quotation. This must be done by notification within the seven-day period for acceptance. Under clause 3.2 of Schedule 2 the architect must confirm immediately, and in writing, the employer's acceptance. The notification, referred to as 'a confirmed acceptance', must state:

1   that the contractor is to carry out the variation;

2   the value of the variation including any amount in lieu of loss and/or expense;

3   preparation costs to be reimbursed;

4   any adjustment of the completion date, and relevant adjustment of any nominated subcontractors' contract periods; and

5   where relevant, that the contractor is to accept any nominated subcontractor's quotation contained in his Schedule 2 quotation.

Rejection of the quotation

If the employer does not accept the Schedule 2 quotation within the seven-day period for acceptance, it is rejected by default. The architect must, however, act to tie up loose ends by instructing whether or not the variation is to be carried out. If the variation is to be implemented in any event, albeit the contractor's quotation is not accepted, the architect must instruct that the variation is to be executed and valued by the quantity surveyor using the basic method.

If the variation is not required at all, the architect must instruct accordingly. The general position at common law is that a tenderer bears the costs of preparing a quotation in the hope that he will recover in earnings from successful bids. The JCT apparently took the view that the instruction of the architect to expend the contractor's resources on preparing a quotation warrants reimbursement of preparation costs even if the quotation is rejected. Thus, under Schedule 2 a fair and reasonable amount in respect of preparation costs must be added to the contract sum. It is not clear whether the fair and reasonable amount to be paid to the contractor for preparation costs is the same fair and reasonable amount which the contractor included in the Schedule 2 quotation pursuant to clause 2.4 of Schedule 2. Since there is no reference to clause 2.4 of Schedule 2 in clause 5 of Schedule 2, it may be assumed that the fair and reasonable amount in clause 5 of Schedule 2 must be objective and need not be based entirely on the amount stated in the contractor's quotation. By analogy with the concept of 'fair' and/or 'reasonable' valuation of certain variations discussed later, a fair and reasonable amount in this context may be equated to cost plus overheads and profit.

There is a caveat to the entitlement to preparation costs: the quotation must have been prepared on a fair and reasonable basis. The contractor may be denied his preparation costs if his quotation has not been prepared on a fair and reasonable basis. Clause 5 of Schedule 2 states that non-acceptance by the employer is not of itself evidence that the quotation was not prepared on a fair and reasonable basis. Unfortunately, the contract does not provide any guidance on what constitutes a 'fair and reasonable basis' of preparing a Schedule 2 quotation. The writers suggest that what constitutes a 'fair and reasonable basis' is either/or:

1   the quality of quotation in terms of accuracy, justification, practicality and cost-effectiveness; and/or
2   the efficiency of the process of producing it,
3   in each case, judged by the standards of an ordinarily competent contractor in the shoes of the contractor.

By such a test, the contractor would not be entitled to recover preparation costs if he produces a quotation that an ordinarily competent contractor would reasonably be expected to rule out as likely to be acceptable. This is the situation where it can reasonably be concluded that the contractor produced the quotation with the expectation that it will almost certainly be rejected. The same would apply to the extent that, by the standards of the ordinarily competent contractor, the cost were not reasonably and necessarily incurred.

Schedule 2 quotation – further variation

There is always the possibility that a variation, regardless of whether it is to be dealt with under the Schedule 2 procedure, may affect work which itself forms part of another previously confirmed Schedule 2 quotation. Clause 5.3.3 requires the quantity surveyor to value such later variation, not under the valuation rules but on a fair and reasonable basis (consideration of fairness and reasonableness in this context is expressly required to have regard to the relevant clause 13A quotation), having regard to the content of the relevant Schedule 2 quotation. The quantity surveyor must also include any direct loss and/or expense incurred by the contractor as a result of the variation. Why variations on variations should be treated differently from any other variation is unclear. This provision can have far reaching effect on the value of the works, for it is common for varied work to be further varied. If on a project a large number of variations are instructed under the Schedule 2 quotation procedure, the result could be a high proportion of the total work in variations calculated on a fair and reasonable basis, rather than under the Schedule 2 quotation rules or even under the quotation procedure. The architect would therefore be well advised not to initiate the Schedule 2 quotation if there is any uncertainty about the work involved.

The basic method

This method involves application of 13 distinct rules stated in clauses 5.6.1 to clause 5.10. To decide which of the rules to apply in any given situation, one has, first, to identify the category to which the work belongs. The possible categories are:

1 additional or substituted work, which can be properly valued by measurement;
2 work for which an approximate quantity is provided in the contract bills;
3 omitted work;
4 additional or substituted work, which cannot be properly valued by measurement; and
5 performance specified work.

The variation rules

Rules 1, 2, 3, 4, 5 apply to additional or substituted work which can be properly valued by measurement. These rules have survived virtually unaltered from the earlier editions of the contract.

Rule 1 is stated in clause 5.6.1.1 as:

> 'Where the additional or substituted work, is of similar character to, is executed under similar conditions as, and does not significantly change the quantity of work set out in the contract bills the rates and prices for the work so set out shall determine the Valuation.'

Rule 2 is given in clause 5.6.1.2 as:

> 'Where the additional or substituted work is of a similar character to work set out in the contract bills but is not executed under similar conditions thereto and/or significantly changes the quantity thereof, the rates and prices for the work so set out shall be the basis for determining the valuation and valuation shall include a fair allowance for such difference in conditions and/or quantity.'

Rule 3 is stated in clause 5.6.1.3 as:

> 'Where the additional or substituted work is not of a similar character to work set out in the contract bills the work shall be valued at fair rates and prices.'

Rules 4 and 5 apply to work for which an approximate quantity is provided in the contract bills. Rule 4 is stated in clause 5.6.1.4 as:

> 'Where the Approximate Quantity is a reasonably accurate forecast of the quantity of work required the rate or price for the Approximate Quantity shall determine the Valuation.'

Rule 5 is in clause 5.6.1.5, which states:

> 'Where the Approximate Quantity is not a reasonably accurate forecast of the quantity of work required the rate or price for the Approximate Quantity shall be the

basis for determining the Valuation and the Valuation shall include a fair allowance for such difference in quantity.'

Rule 6, contained in clause 5.6.2, requires omitted work to be valued at the rates and prices for such work set out in the contract bills.

Rules 7 to 9 apply to:

1   additional or substituted work which can be properly valued by measurement;
2   work for which an approximate quantity is included in the contract bills; and
3   omitted work.

Rule 7 (clause 5.6.3.1) requires such work to be measured in accordance with the same principles as those used in the preparation of the contract bills.

Rule 8 (clause 5.6.3.2) requires allowances to be made for any percentage or lump sum adjustments to the contract sum. The contract does not provide any guidance on how the allowance is to be quantified. Many quantity surveyors apply a factor to the valuation produced by the other rules to arrive at the allowance, which may be an addition or a deduction. This factor is often the proportion that the difference between the original contract sum (or part thereof) and the accepted contract sum (or part thereof) bears to the original contract sum (or part thereof).

Rule 9 (clause 5.6.3.3) requires the adjustment of certain categories of preliminary items where the nature of the variation makes such adjustment appropriate. The types of preliminary items that are adjustable are those referred to in section A of the Standard Method of Measurement 7th edition. However, adjustment of the preliminary items is expressly forbidden where the valuation is of work carried out in compliance with an architect's instruction as to the expenditure of a provisional sum for defined work. The justification for this is that the contractor ought reasonably to have allowed for the impact of the relevant work on the preliminaries. Unfortunately, there are at least two problems of construction with this rule. First, does 'addition or reduction of preliminary items' cover new items and omitted items or does it also cover mere changes in the duration or other parameter of items already in contract bills? Secondly, the contract fails to specify the nature of the 'allowances' to be made. In contrast to 'fair allowance' referred to in clause 5.6.1.2, there is no requirement that the allowance under this rule is fair. Should it then be the additional costs incurred as a consequence of the variation or a quantification based on the prices and rates in the contract bills?

Rule 10 covers 'additional or substituted work which cannot be properly valued by measurement'. By clause 5.7, such work is to be valued on a dayworks basis. Dayworks is a method of paying for work based on the prime costs of all labour, plant and materials used in carrying out the work, normally with a percentage addition to the total of each of these three resource groups for the contractor's overheads and profit. The rates and prices of the resources are usually contained in a document referred to as a 'dayworks schedule' applicable to the contract. A dayworks schedule may be drawn up specifically for a particular project. However, it is established practice to contract on the basis of a published standard schedule, but allowing tenderers wishing to be paid at different rates to state, in the bills of quantities, percentages for additions or deductions on the total amounts for each resource group determined in accordance with the standard schedule.

JCT 98 incorporates the use of standard schedules which are to be adjusted in accordance with any percentage additions or deductions inserted in the contract bills. For general work, it is the edition of *Definition or Prime Cost of Daywork Carried Out Under a Building Contract* issued by RICS and the Construction Confederation which was current on the base date (this date is stated in the appendix to the contract). Where the work is of a specialist nature the schedule to be used is the schedule issued by RICS and the appropriate body representing organisations in that trade and current on the base date (clause 5.7.2). RICS and the following bodies have agreed schedules:

1   the Electrical Contractors Association;
2   the Electrical Contractors Association of Scotland;
3   the Heating and Ventilating Contractors Association.

Contractors will often claim that work cannot be properly valued by measurement by reason of a change to conditions under which it is carried out, or that it is of a different character. Such claims must fail since those are the precise circumstances covered by Rules 1 to 3 for application to measured work. Quantity surveyors, on the other hand, will sometimes strain to achieve measurement to avoid resorting to the dayworks method, which is to be used only where the work cannot properly be valued by measurement. The result can be a measurement by approximation, or assertion that measurement can be made simply because some form of measurement has been made! It is submitted that the meaning of 'properly' in this context means measurement by the rules in the applicable standard method, using descriptions categorised in those rules, but applied only where the nature of the work would allow accurate physical measurement. In practice, the difficulty often lies in identifiable parameters. For example, a variation may relate to damage to completed plasterwork. If the boundaries are clear, such as replacement of a whole wall, then measurement will be possible; but if the damage is in undefined patches, requiring cutting back to firm bonded plaster, the areas may not be measurable in the practical sense.

Rule 11 (clause 5.9) applies to the impact on other work arising from a variation, an architect's instruction as to the expenditure of provisional sums or a difference between an approximate quantity and the actual quantity required. Where the impact is in the form of changes to the conditions under which such other work is to be carried out (what amounts to 'change of conditions'), the work is to be treated as a variation instructed under clause 3.10 and valued accordingly. As a consequence of the proviso in clause 5.10.2, productivity losses from changed conditions are to be claimed for under clause 4.23.

Rule 12 (clause 5.8) applies where contractor's designed portion work is varied. The rules in the basic method also apply to such variations. However, there are the additional requirements that the valuation:

1 must allow for relevant design-related work such as preparation of drawings; and
2 '... shall be consistent with rates and prices of work of a similar character set out in the contract bills or the analysis'.

Rule 13 (clause 5.10.1) states:

> 'To the extent that the Valuation does not relate to the execution of additional or substituted work or the omission of work or to the extent that the valuation of

any work or liabilities directly associated with a variation cannot reasonably be effected in the Valuation by the application of clauses 5.6 to 5.9 a fair valuation shall be made.'

An example of an application of this rule is where work is omitted after the contractor has already incurred liability towards carrying it out. This rule would allow the contractor to be paid in respect of wasted costs of:

1 dealing with orders;
2 planning specifically for the omitted work; and
3 resources already procured but no longer required.

It would also apply to increased costs arising from variations affecting access to the site, working space, working hours and order of carrying out the works as stated in the contract.

Similar character/conditions

The application of the rules, particularly rules 1 to 5, raises a number of problems of interpretation. The first, which has been the subject of considerable debate among commentators over the years, concerns the meaning of the phrase 'similar character'. For example, an interpretation put forward by Powell-Smith and Sims is that the words 'similar character . . . must mean that the description of the item in question is identical in every respect to that of an item in the contract bills'. This is essentially the same interpretation as Hibberd's (Hibberd, P. *Variations in Construction Contracts,* Collins, London, 1986, pp. 103–104), who wrote:

> 'The test must surely be whether the work if measured at the bill preparation stage would have been lost among the items which went to make up the quantity of work described or would of necessity have required a separate bill description on account of its different character.'

The opposing view is that exact match of description is not necessary for items of work to be of a similar character and that they only have to be 'of a like nature' (Parris, J. *The Standard Form of Building Contract* (2nd edition), Collins, London, 1985, p. 162). In the subsequent edition of Powell-Smith and Sims' *Building Contract Claims*, the phrase is equated with 'virtually identical' (Chappell, D. M. *Powell-Smith and Sims' Building Contract Claims* (3rd edition), BSP, Oxford, 1998, p. 111). It is submitted that, in the absence of a precise legal meaning and a contractual definition, the term 'similar character' must be made to bear a meaning that reflects the common practice and understanding of the construction industry unless that meaning clearly conflicts with the contract. An example will show that the description of the item arrived at by applying the appropriate standard method of measurement is not in itself conclusive. Consider substitution of a ground floor concrete beam with a beam of the same dimensions but in concrete of a slightly different mix not included in the contract bills. Deciding the issue by the description alone entails valuation by 'fair rates and prices' (as to the approach to the correct method of determining 'fair rates and prices' see below) and not on the basis of the pricing of the concrete originally required under the contract. In practice, the bill rates for the concrete originally required would be the basis of pricing of the new item, with allowances for the differences in the quantities of the materials required.

The same problem arises regarding the application of the description 'similar' to conditions under which the work is done. For a start, on the question of what exactly the term 'conditions' covers, the commentators disagree hopelessly. Parris wrote that they must be conditions set out in the contract bills, whilst in the 5th and 6th editions of *Keating on Building Contracts* (Sweet & Maxwell), it is suggested that it refers to site and weather conditions. Yet another interpretation (*Powell-Smith and Sims' Building Contract Claims*) is that the terms cover a miscellany of different type of conditions, e.g. site, weather, working space, and the contractor's work methods, under which the contractor could reasonably be expected to have anticipated to carry out the works at the time of preparing his tender. Still on the question of conditions, the position which results if the contractor could have done the work under similar conditions as work in the contract bills but chose to do it another way is far from clear, e.g. doing in winter what could have been done in summer. According to the wording of the clause, the actual conditions under which the variation is actually done should be considered. There is no reference to the reasonableness of the contractor's choice.

This debate was considered in the first instance decision of *Wates Construction (South) v Bredero Fleet* [1993] 63 BLR 133 which was an appeal on a point of law against an arbitrator's interpretation of the valuation rules under the 1980 edition of the contract. The arbitrator decided the question of whether there was a change of 'conditions' under clause 13.5 by reference to:

1 the conditions the contractor had in mind when pricing his tender;
2 knowledge gained from negotiations;
3 the express terms of the contract bills; and
4 physical conditions relating to time, the contract period, the nature of the works and other matters impinging upon the working environment.

His Honour Judge Forbes QC held that any information as to conditions not stated in the contract was inadmissible extrinsic evidence and that therefore the arbitrator had erred in law by considering such evidence. He stated that the 'conditions' referred to in clause 13.5.5 were the conditions under which the relevant contract works were to be executed, as could be determined from the express provisions of the contract bills, drawings and other contract documents.

Significance of change of quantity

The conditions are silent as to the guidelines to be applied in deciding whether or not a change of quantity is significant. The percentage change is a possible guide. However, there are many types of work where the same percentage change is, in cost terms, significant in one situation and insignificant in another. For example, a 100 per cent increase in the value of fill material may be insignificant if there is no limit to the supply of the material from the borrow pit. However, where the supply was just enough for the volume in the contract bills, even a 10 per cent increase would be significant as the contractor would have to find another source of supply. Perhaps, the significance has to be assessed by also examining the impact of the change on the contractor's prior arrangements regarding the work in question.

Fair rates, prices and allowances

The leading commentators have interpreted 'fair valuation' in construction contracts with similar variation valuation clauses as cost plus overheads and profit. Commenting on 'fair valuation' under the Institution of Civil Engineers' conditions of contract (5th edition) (ICE 5), Mr Max Abrahamson wrote that it will normally mean 'cost plus a reasonable percentage for profit (but not contingencies if the work is being valued after it has been carried out on an actual not estimated costs) with a deduction for any proven inefficiency by the contractor, but if there is proof of a general market rate for comparable work it may be taken into consideration or applied completely' (Abrahamson, M. W., *Engineering Law and the ICE Contracts*, Chapman & Hall, London, 1995). This approach has received some judicial support. In *Henry Boot Construction v Alstom Combined Cycles Ltd* [2005] EWCA Civ 814 His Honour Judge Humphrey Lloyd QC stated that 'a fair valuation generally means a valuation which will not give the contractor more than his actual costs reasonably and necessarily incurred plus similar allowance for overheads and profit'. He has since repeated the approach in two other cases: *Floods Queensferry Ltd v Shand Construction Ltd* [1999] BLR 315; *Weldon Plant Ltd v The Commissioner For the New Towns* (2000) 77 Con LR 1 (hereafter '*Weldon v CNT*'). In *Weldon v CNT*, he had to deal with the required proof of overheads recoverable. The arbitrator in that case had, in arriving at his award, taken the view that the contractor needed to prove incurrence of the overheads claimed as part of a fair valuation under the 6th edition of the Institution of Civil Engineers' conditions of contract (ICE 6). His Honour accepted that incurrence of additional time-related overheads had to be proved. He however stated (at p. 12) that fixed overheads did not require proof beyond an approximate assessment such as 'deriving a percentage from accounts of the contractor including where appropriate associated companies that provide services or the like that qualify as overheads'.

An issue yet to be considered by the courts concerns fair valuation where the contractor had under-estimated costs as a whole. If the contractor had under-bid by a lump sum deduction against the total of the prices of each work item in the contract bills, rule 8 requires allowances to be made for such reduction. The problem arises where the reduction is effected by a proportionate reduction of each rate or price without indication that such adjustment has been made. Writers have doubted the appropriateness of the cost plus overheads and profits approach in such a context. It is suggested in Hudson's *Building and Engineering Contracts* that a fair valuation must have regard to the contractor's general pricing level (Wallace, I. N. D., *Hudson's Building and Engineering Contracts* (11th edition), Sweet & Maxwell, London, 1995, para. 7.105.). A valuation below actual cost would therefore be fair where the contract price is below actual costs or market pricing.

Other sources of disputes

Apart from the problems of interpretation, a number of factors relating to contract practice make the application of these rules prone to disputes. These include:

1   access to the contractor's pricing data;
2   the consistency of prices in the contract bills;
3   the pricing method of the contract bills;
4   errors in the contract bills;
5   design and build;
6   minor works; and
7   dayworks sheets.

Access to the contractor's pricing data

A new rate determined by the application of rule 2 or 3 is referred to in the industry as a 'star rate'. The rate-fixing methods most commonly used in industry are the pro-rata and the bill analysis approaches. With the pro-rata approach, new rates are obtained by taking the arithmetic average of the rates of two or more items in the contract bills. The bill analysis approach involves an examination of the synthesis of the rates in the contract bills to determine the assumptions, e.g. all-in rates and prices for resources, materials usage and wastage rates, and labour and equipment productivities, which would have been applicable to the variation work had the contractor been required to price it at the tendering stage.

Unfortunately, the contractor is not obliged to supply such pricing data, which is considered by many contractors as commercially sensitive. In *Boot v Alstom*, the issue of the contractor's failure to provide details of the make-up of a price in the contract for the purpose of valuing variations in accordance with the equivalent of rule 2 in the ICE 6 was raised. An arbitrator decided that the fact that the rate or price for work of similar character was a mistake made it unreasonable to use it as a basis for valuation of variations in accordance with the equivalent of rule 2. He added that, the effect of the mistake aside, absence of details of the pricing of the relevant work made its use as a basis unreasonable because it was impossible to extract rates and prices for variations in a manner that could inspire confidence. This proposition was rejected in the TCC. The particular contract, as an amendment to ICE 6, imposed upon the contractor an obligation to submit any build-ups of rates required by the engineer. His Honour Judge Humphrey Lloyd QC stated that, even without such an obligation, the engineer would still be under a duty to determine new rates without necessarily having the build-ups of the rates upon which the new rate is to be based. That question was not addressed completely in the Court of Appeal because, as the arbitrator had failed to apply rule 2 on the grounds of a mistake in the relevant contract rate or price, they did not have to. However, Beldam LJ accepted ([2000] BLR 247 at 257) that it was open to the arbitrator to have formed the opinion that he could not say how far it was reasonable to use the lump sum in the valuation of the varied work. It is then for the party asserting reasonableness to prove it. This suggests that the engineer would be entitled to determine the new rate from his own experience, but making allowance for the pricing level represented by the prices in the contract. An arbitrator or court would find it difficult to ignore a price arrived at in this way without the relevant details from the contractor. Furthermore, failure to supply the build-ups during the interlocutory stages of litigation may be taken into account in the awarding of costs.

Consistency of prices in the contract bills

The valuation of variations can be difficult and contentious if the rates and prices in the contract bills are inconsistent. An example of a possible consistency is where the rate for an item in one section of the contract bills differs significantly from a similar item in another section without a logical explanation for the difference. Sometimes, such inconsistencies are the result of tactical estimating decisions made by the contractor at an adjudication stage of the tendering process. Rate loading is a well-known form of this tactical approach to estimating usually resorted to for the purpose of improving the contractor's cash flow during construction. This entails raising the rates in some parts of the tender bills of quantities and decreasing the prices in others correspondingly. For example, by increasing the prices of work at the earlier stage of the programme by a certain percentage and removing the total added on from the prices of work expected to be carried out towards the end of the project, the contractor gets paid more than the real value of the work at the earlier stages. In this way, the contractor's capital lock-up is reduced. This form of rate loading is referred to as 'front-end' rate loading.

Back-end rate loading is the opposite of this strategy. Here, the prices of work to be done towards the end of the contract period are increased at the expense of work to be done at the beginning. The result of this course of action would be to increase the contractor's capital lock-up. An unusual situation where a contractor may wish to do this is where the cost of borrowing is so low and the inflation adjustment regime so generous that the contractor stands to gain from inflation adjustments exceeding the increased capital lock-up.

It is the duty of the client's professional advisers to undertake a detailed inspection of the bills of quantities prices to identify possible inconsistencies, which should then be taken up with the contractor concerned before the contract is executed. Where this is not done, exceedingly low prices or exceedingly high prices could present problems when the work involved is subject to substantial variation.

The pricing method of the contract bills

A common problem with the valuation of variations is that changes in quantities of work often produce disproportionate changes of total cost. The extent of this problem depends on how closely the contract bills model the real way costs are incurred on construction work. On the whole, the solution prescribed for this problem is based on the recognition of three different types of construction costs in the compilation and pricing of bills of quantities:

1 costs that vary proportionally to the length of time over which the associated permanent works are being executed, e.g. equipment rental, and running and operating costs;
2 costs which are fixed where the quantities of the associated work may vary within limits, e.g. setting up and removal costs of plant; and
3 costs, which vary proportionally to the quantities of the permanent works, e.g. costs of materials in such work.

Barnes (Barnes, M., *CESMM3 Handbook* (2nd edition), Thomas Telford, London, 1992) explains how this approach reduces the need for star rates and, correspondingly, the incidence of disputes concerning the valuation of variations. SMM 7 adopts this pricing approach.

Errors in the contract bills

JCT SBC 05 recognises two categories of 'mistakes':

1 errors due to departures from the applicable standard method of measurement and mistakes of computation made by the employer's professional advisers (employer's errors); and
2 computational errors made by the contractor in his tender (contractor's errors).

By clause 2.14.1 of JCT SBC 05, the employer's errors are to be corrected and the affected work treated as a variation. The only problem with this type of mistake often concerns disagreement as to whether or not there have been mistakes. For example, to the contractor's claim that there is an omission from the contract bills, the architect may reply that the allegedly missing item is indispensably necessary to complete other expressly described work. This brings up the knotty problem of exactly what operations are, or are not included in a bill item. Commenting on the similar problem in relation to ICE 5, Mr Max Abrahamson wrote that the answer to the question must be decided by reference to the ordinary meaning of the words used in the descriptions of the bill items concerned, the standard method of measurement and the standard legal rules of interpretation (Abrahamson, M. W., *Engineering Law and the ICE Contracts* (4th edition), Applied Science Publishers, London, 1979, p. 207).

It is a common understanding within the construction professions that one of the main purposes for bills of quantities in construction contracts is for the purpose of valuing variations. The position at common law is therefore that the contractor and employer are equally bound by errors in the bills of quantities. This position is illustrated by the decision of the Court of Appeal in *Dudley v Parsons and Morrin Ltd* (CA, 1967, unreported) in which a contractor under a predecessor of JCT 98 had inserted in the tender bills of quantities a rate of 2 shillings per cubic yard extra over for excavation in rock. A fair price was £2. The architect had valued at a fair rate all the quantity over the provisional quantity in the bill. The contractor sought the whole quantity at a fair rate. Pearce LJ said:

> 'Naturally one sympathises with the contractor in the circumstances, but one must assume that he chose to

take the risk of greatly under-pricing an item which might not arise, whereby he lowered the tender by £1,425. He may well have thought it worthwhile to take that risk in order to increase his chances of securing the contract.'

Clearly, the court was influenced in this case by the provisional nature of the quantities in the bill, but the outcome was that the bill rates were held to apply to the total quantity. The whole principle of using pricing levels in the contract for variations would be undermined if it were otherwise. Once the contract is concluded, and provided the employer was not aware, and taking advantage, of a patent error in accepting the erroneous tender, the rate is accepted as a risk borne by both parties. This common law position was reiterated recently by the Court of Appeal in the *Boot v Alstom* litigation.

Clause 4.2 binds both the contractor and the employer to the contractor's errors. It states:

'The Contract Sum shall not be adjusted or altered in any way whatsoever otherwise than in accordance with the express provisions of the Conditions, and subject to clause 2.14 any error whether of arithmetic or otherwise in the computation of the Contract Sum shall be deemed to have been accepted by the parties.'

An erroneously high bill rate must therefore stand although the contractor would have no right of objection if the architect omitted quantities in order to save money for the employer. This point was confirmed in the *Boot v Alstom* litigation in relation to the ICE 6, which has rules for the valuation of variations corresponding almost exactly to rules 1, 2 and 3 explained above. The project from which the case arose was the construction at Connah's Quay in Clwyd of a power station that was to comprise four sets of combined cycle turbines. Each set comprised a turbine hall, a heat recovery steam generator (HRSG) and cooling towers. As a result of a post-tender amendment made by Alstom before contract formation, additional sheet piling was required in all three areas of each set. Boot priced all the additional work in each set at £250,880. By mistake, Boot put forward the price as applicable to only the turbine hall area. The price was accepted by Alstom and incorporated into the contract subsequently entered into without being alerted to the fact that the work was described as covering only the turbine hall. The dispute referred to arbitration concerned valuation of the additional sheet piling in the HRSG and cooling towers areas as a variation. It was common ground that rule 1 did not apply. A very experienced arbitrator decided that the £250,880 (the price for the additional sheeting piling in the turbine hall area) could not be used for valuing the remainder of the additional sheet piling on the ground that the price was a mistake. This is how he justified ignoring the price:

> 'If one is not seeking to apply the price directly to the work in question, then the work in question must, by definition, be different from the work included within the ambit of the price. If the work is sufficiently different to warrant an adjustment of the price, what one would expect to reach would be a modified price. But that would be satisfactory or reasonable (to use the phrasing of the clause) only if one could be confident about the satisfactory nature of the route taken to the original price. That confidence is not available here. On the contrary one knows that the route to the original price was flawed by at least one mistake. That seems to me to undermine the applicability of the price in any extended role in the contract. To put it another way, while one cannot change the mistake, I do not see it as "reasonable" to enlarge its ambit and thereby compound the effect of the error. I anticipate that the contractor who underestimated a price by error would see the force of the argument and would be as vehement in opposing its extension beyond the ambit of the original mistake, as [the employer] is vehement in opposing the use of £250,880 in this case . . . Given that the rule must be the same whichever way the error goes, it seems to me that it is "reasonable" not to use a price where the price has been reached by a mistake or error.'

On appeal, on a question of law to the TCC ((2000) 69 Con LR 27), His Honour Judge Humphrey Lloyd QC upheld the contractor's challenge. An appeal to the Court of Appeal was dismissed by a majority. Lloyd LJ rephrased the logic of the first instance decision with which he agreed completely in these terms:

> 'The meaning of rule 2 does not, I think, admit of much doubt. It provides a half-way house between rule 1 and rule 3. Like rule 1, rule 2 is mandatory. It applies when work covered by the variation order is of a different

character from the work priced in the Bill of Quantities, or is executed under different conditions. If the differences are relatively small, the Engineer is obliged to use the rates set out in the Bill of Quantities as the basis for his valuation, making such adjustment as may be necessary to take account of the differences. But the differences may be very great, as, for example, where the variation order calls for the excavation of foundations in solid rock, instead of clay. In those circumstances, the Engineer may take the view that it would not be "reasonable" to base his valuation on the rates contained in the Bill of Quantities. He is then thrown back on rule 3. That is the sole function of the words "so far as may be reasonable" in rule 2. They call for a comparison between the work covered by the variation order and the work priced in the Bill of Quantities. They do not enable the Engineer to open up or disregard the rates on the ground that they were inserted by mistake.'

His Lordship drew support for his interpretation of the rules from a need to avoid the uncertainty in the administration that would otherwise result. At p. 251 he said:

'Any other view would have far reaching consequences. If the Engineer were free to open up rates at the request of one party or the other because they were inserted in the Bill of Quantities by mistake, it would not only unsettle the basis of competitive tendering, but create the sort of uncertainty in the administration of building contracts which should be avoided at all costs . . .'

This uncertainty is likely to be compounded by the fact that it is often impossible for the engineer to determine whether a particular 'mistake' is indeed a genuine error or the result of motives and assumptions underlying the tender. Two factors contribute to the difficulty. The first is the practice of rate loading already discussed. The second relates to the fact that contractors sometimes quote below costs for various reasons, e.g. lack of work, prestige value of the project, and a desire to break into new markets. The difficulty of the employer or his professional advisers in deciding whether or not a low rate is the result of a mistake is therefore great. Where they do not admit knowledge of a genuine mistake before entering into the contract, it is unlikely that any court would impute such knowledge to them.

Even where an error is binding, contractors often argue that whilst they are prepared to stand by their mistake in the tender it is unfair to value variations on the basis of their mistake. This argument goes against the common understanding in the construction industry that one of the main reasons for the practice of including bills of quantities in contractual documents in construction contracts is for the purpose of valuing variations. However, taking full advantage of contractual rights may not always be in the best interests of the parties. A contractor insisting on the high rate may be jeopardising future relations whilst a contractor who is held to excessively low rates may resort to claims and sub-standard work to minimise the effect of his error. Depending on the gravity of the error, the contractor may even go into liquidation with all the adverse financial consequences that flow from that. Hence, a possible reason for the parties agreeing a method of valuation other than under clause 5.6 may relate to serious mistakes in the contract bills.

Is it a fair valuation on the basis of the contract bills? Trickey and Hackett (Trickey, G. and Hackett, M., *The Presentation and Settlement of Contractors' Claims* (2nd edition), Spon Press, London, 2001) advise that one should ask the question: 'At what rate would the tenderer have priced this item had he known at the stage of tender that the work (now subject of a variation) was required?' Answering this question would entail an examination of the make-up of the contractor's tender:

1   unit labour costs;
2   labour output rates;
3   unit costs of materials;
4   waste factors on materials;
5   plant hire rates;
6   the level of supervision and other preliminary items;
7   the provision of temporary works; and
8   mark-up.

This approach can have contractual force by implication, provided that its use does not contradict the express provisions of the particular contract.

Design and Build

Payment under this contract is dealt with under clause 4. The process is similar to JCT SBC 05 except that no architect or quantity surveyor is involved. Effectively, the valuation is to be undertaken by the contractor. If the employer disagrees with the contractor's valuation he (or the employer's agent on his behalf) can issue a payment notice in a different sum and/or serve a withholding notice. The standard valuation rules are set out in clauses 4.13 and 4.14. However, the employer only has five days after the receipt of the application from the contractor to issue a payment notice in a different sum (clause 4.10.3). If the employer fails to issue this notice in time or at all then the contractor will be entitled to be paid the sum applied for (clause 4.10.5) subject to the employer's right to withhold.

If, in Appendix 1, the supplementary provisions are said to apply, provision S4 governs the valuation of change instructions. It is triggered by the issue of an instruction from the employer. If he, or the contractor, believes that a valuation, extension of time or loss and/or expense will be entailed, the contractor has 14 days to submit an estimate of the value, extension of time, loss and/or expense details of the resources required and a method statement. The employer has 10 days to agree or he must:

1   instruct compliance and clause 4 will apply; or
2   withdraw his instruction.

If the instruction is withdrawn, the contractor is entitled to be paid for any abortive design work. The sting in the tail is that if the contractor fails to submit the required estimates, the valuation is to be carried out under clause 5, extensions of time under clauses 2.23 to 2.26 and loss and/or expense under clauses 3.9 and 4.19, but no payment is to be made until the final account and final statement.

Minor Works

Under JCT MW 05 variations are empowered by clause 3.6. It is a very short clause allowing the architect to vary the works by addition, omission or change to the order or period in which they are to be carried out. The contractor has no right of reasonable objection, but he can always refer any dispute to arbitration.

Valuation of variations may be carried out by the architect and contractor reaching agreement before the work is carried out or, failing agreement by the architect, on a fair and reasonable basis using the prices in the priced specification, schedules or schedule of rates where relevant. The architect's view as to whether the particular priced document is 'relevant' in any particular instance will, doubtless, prevail, at least until adjudication. The contractor is not in a strong position and, even if priced schedules are used, the employer does not warrant that they are correct. A major difficultly, from the contractor's point of view is that he is deemed to have included in his price for carrying out and completing the works in accordance with the contract documents. Thus, work shown on the drawing, but not in the schedules, does not rank as a variation as would be the case under JCT SBC 05 with quantities edition for example (see above also in relation to the inclusion of loss and/or expense).

Dayworks

By clause 5.7 of JCT SBC 05 with quantities, the contractor is expected to deliver to the architect or his authorised representative (usually the quantity surveyor or the clerk of works), not later than the end of the week following that in which the work was done, vouchers on work to be valued on a daywork basis. Such vouchers, called 'dayworks sheets' in the industry, specify all the resources used, including names of operatives and supervisory personnel and lists of plant and materials used. There are many who believe that the timetable for the submission of dayworks sheets is too lax. For instance, if the contractor carries out dayworks on a Monday, he has up until the Friday of the following week to submit the sheets: 12 days!

As the contractor would need to know that the work is to be valued on a dayworks basis in order to keep the records required, it appears that the contractor must be informed of this fact before the work is commenced. This question is a possible explanation of the common practice whereby architects issue instructions containing express stipulations that the work is to be done as daywork. However, it has to be pointed out that, unless the architect is authorised by the employer to reach agreements on his behalf with the contractor regarding the use of valuation methods other than those in clause 13.5, the quantity surveyor is not obliged to use this basis of valuation. For example, if the work is additional or substituted work which can be valued by measurement, the quantity surveyor must use rules 1 to 3. In practice, many contractors maintain timesheets for their own cost control purposes. To play safe, relevant timesheets are presented as dayworks sheets whenever it appears that the relevant work cannot be properly valued by measurement. The result is often a pile of unsigned dayworks vouchers which the architect resists signing on grounds such as that relevant work: (i) is not a variation; or (ii) is measurable; or (iii) was done when he was not present.

This last reason is one frequently faced by contractors, even in circumstances where the work is clearly not measurable. The contractor should not worry; he is entitled to rely on his vouchers whether signed or not. The purpose of giving the architect (or the clerk of works) an opportunity to verify a voucher is to protect the employer's interest, and the architect who avoids signing vouchers on the grounds of absence from site runs the risk of putting himself in breach of his contract with the employer.

A view sometimes held by architects and quantity surveyors is that before signing a dayworks voucher, there is a right or even a duty to correct the contents of the voucher to what they consider is a fair amount. For example, a voucher may show ten hours labour carrying out what should, in the architect's opinion, have been completed easily within three hours. However, it is not for the architect, or the quantity surveyor, to change the hours or any other entry on the voucher, unless the entry is not a correct representation of what actually occurred. The point was considered by the Court of Appeal in *Clusky (t/a Damian Construction) v Chamberlain* (unreported, 24 November 1994), in which it was said that the trial judge had gone behind daywork timesheets:

> '[The trial judge was] ... wrong to go behind the timesheets. The timesheets were not suggested to be fake. The most that could be said ... was that perhaps the workmen did not work as expeditiously as they might have done. That is the danger of day-work contracts. It is a danger which is often dealt with by the architect, making sure that the men are on site and working.'

Clearly, the quantity surveyor's duty in these circumstances (if daywork is the appropriate method of evaluation) is to apply the contract daywork rates to the hours on the voucher, provided it is an accurate record of the time taken. This will be so even if he considers the hours to be unreasonably high. If the hours recorded are not a true record of the time expended, then the contractor may be guilty of a criminal offence under the Theft Act 1968 (e.g. s. 15(1) – Obtaining property by deception; s. 17(1) – False accounting).

A particular problem presented by the system of dayworks is that it requires very meticulous record keeping on the part of the architect or quantity surveyor, where the architect delegates the verification of dayworks to him. On large jobs, it is often exceedingly difficult to keep track of instructions involving dayworks. In many cases the administration has to be delegated to several people. The combination of sheer numbers of dayworks in those circumstances, the geographical spread of the site, hectic pace of work often requiring the issue of instructions otherwise than in writing, and the multiplicity of contracting organisations on the site, creates a working environment which can easily be exploited by the contractor and his subcontractors. There is therefore the real danger of unauthorised dayworks sheets slipping through. This is helped by the fact that the contractor may have up to 12 days to submit dayworks sheets for verification.

Conclusions

Application of the traditional valuation rules in the JCT Standard Form of Building Contract does not always produce clear answers. It is remarkable that, considering the controversy among commentators, there has been very little reported litigation on some of the areas of uncertainty.

Frequently asked questions

Q. If the contractor's surveyor and the employer's surveyor agree on the valuation of variation during valuations of interim payments is it subsequently open to one or either of them to revisit the valuation of those variations for the purposes of the final account?

A. It depends on the terms of the contract, the process adopted and the intentions and authority of the individual surveyors. Some contracts will state that agreements reached on the valuation of variations are final and binding as between the parties. In the absence of fraud or dishonesty the parties cannot revisit the agreed valuation of variations on such contracts. There is no such general provision in JCT contracts although quotations provided and accepted using the JCT SBC Schedule 2 procedure (and other similar procedures in other contracts) will be binding on the parties. If the contractor's surveyor and the employer's surveyor agree a valuation for a variation which they each sign off as agreed for the final account that may be binding on the contractor and employer depending on the levels of authority of the respective surveyors. Even in the absence of express authority to make such agreements the surveyors may have ostensible authority to do so.

Q. Are the employer and contractor bound to value variations using bill rates even if those rates are obviously wrong?

A. Provided that the varied works come within the scope of the clause requiring variations to be priced using bill rates (that is it is of similar character to the work set out in the contract bills) then the rates and prices in the contract bills must be used to value the varied works even if those rates are obviously wrong. This applies to additional works as it does to omitted or varied works. See the decision of the Court of Appeal in *Henry Boot Construction v Alstom Combined Cycles* [2000] BLR 247.

7

Measurement and valuation in the NEC Contract

The NEC applies a radically different procedure for valuing changes under a contract. First, and most important, in common with much about the NEC, the terminology is different. There is no such thing as a variation; this expression has no place in the NEC whose procedure is predicated on the concept of compensation events. These are effectively a composite of variations, extensions of time and loss and expense arising from a change to the works information.

Definition of compensation event

Compensation events are defined within clause 60.1 and apply equally across all of the main options. They are as follows:

1 The project manager gives an instruction changing the works information (except one to accept a defect or a change in the contractor's design requested by the contractor).
2 The employer is late in giving access to the site.
3 The employer has failed to provide something that he has agreed to provide.
4 The project manager gives an instruction to stop or not to start any work or to change a key date.
5 Either the employer or other contractors do not work within the times shown on the accepted programme or do not work within the conditions stated in the works information or carry out work on the site that is not stated in the works information.

6 The project manager or the supervisor does not reply to a communication within the period required by the contract.

7 The project manager gives an instruction for dealing with an object of interest found within the site.

8 The project manager or the supervisor changes a decision which he has previously communicated to the contractor.

9 The project manager withholds an acceptance for a reason not stated in the contract.

10 The supervisor instructs the contractor to search for a defect but no defect is found.

11 A test or inspection done by the supervisor causes unnecessary delay.

12 The contractor encounters physical conditions on site that are not weather conditions and which would have been unreasonable for an experienced contractor, when entering into the contract, to have allowed for.

13 A weather condition is encountered which weather data shows occurs less frequently than once in every ten years.

14 An event occurs which is stated in the contract to be an employer's risk.

15 Part of the works is taken over before completion.

16 The employer does not provide materials, facilities and samples for tests and inspections as stated in the works information.

17 The project manager corrects an assumption made in a compensation event.

18 Any other breach of contract by the employer.

19 Any other event which prevents the contractor from completing the works by the date shown on the accepted programme or prevents him from completing the works at all and which neither party could prevent and which would have been unreasonable for an experienced contractor, when entering into the contract, to have allowed for.

On the issue of a project manager's or supervisor's instruction which is a compensation event the project manager instructs the contractor to submit a quotation.

Other compensation events trigger the early warning system by which either party must notify the other as soon as either becomes aware of an event which could increase the cost to the employer, delay the works beyond the completion date or key dates in the accepted programme or impair the performance of the works. In any event the contractor must notify the project manager of the event which has happened or which he expects to happen within eight weeks of becoming aware of the event. If he does not do so he loses his entitlement to any extra money or time unless the project manager should have notified the event to the contractor but failed to do so. Unless the project manager decides that the event notified by the contractor does not warrant a change to the prices or the dates the project manager instructs the contractor to submit a quotation.

The project manager may also instruct the contractor to submit quotations for proposed instructions or changed decisions. In this case the contractor does not implement the proposed instruction or changed decision until instructed to do so.

When instructing the contractor to submit quotations, if the project manager believes that the effects of the compensation event are too uncertain to be forecast reasonably he states assumptions about the event in his instruction. If any of these assumptions are subsequently found to be wrong the project manager notifies a correction which is itself a compensation event.

Within three weeks of being instructed to do so the contractor submits quotations to the project manager. These quotations comprise proposed changes to the prices and delays to the completion date and key dates and are supported by details of the contractor's assessment and, where the programme is altered, proposed alterations to the accepted programme.

If there are alternative methods of dealing with the compensation event the contractor and the project manager should discuss these first and the project manager may instruct the contractor to submit alternative quotations.

Within two weeks of receiving the contractor's quotation the project manager may either instruct the contractor to submit a revised quotation (after explaining his reasons for doing so), accept the quotation, notify the contractor that the proposed instruction will not be given or notify the contractor that he will be making his own assessment.

If the project manager does not respond within the two-week period the contractor can notify the project manager of his failure to respond. If the project manager fails to respond within an additional two weeks of the contractor's notification the quotation is deemed to have been accepted unless it is a quotation for a proposed instruction or proposed changed decision.

If the contractor does not submit a quotation and details of his assessment within the time allowed or if the project manager decides that the contractor has not assessed the compensation event correctly the project manager assesses the compensation event and notifies the contractor of his assessment and gives him details of it.

Assessing compensation events

Changes to the prices resulting from compensation events are assessed as the effect upon the actual defined cost of the work already done, the forecast defined cost of work not yet done and the resulting fee.

The definition of defined cost is set out in Chapter 4 above but the key point is that unless the parties agree otherwise compensation events are calculated by reference to actual cost or forecast actual cost and not by rates or prices or lump sums in the bills of quantities or other priced documents.

Once a quotation has been accepted it forms a binding agreement and is not subsequently changed (other than to change a project manager's assumption which is itself another compensation event) even if the forecast actual cost or the forecast delay to the works turns out to be over or under-estimated.

Main options B and D – contracts with bill of quantities

Errors in the bills of quantities or departures from the method of measurement are corrected and such corrections are compensation events.

If the total quantity of work done is different from the quantity stated in the bill of quantities and that difference does not result from a change to the works information and that item in the bill of quantities is more than 0.5 per cent of the total of the prices at the contract date then that is a compensation event which justifies a change to the rate in the bill of quantities.

Records

As stated above compensation events are assessed using actual cost and forecast actual cost. The contractor submits details of his assessment with each quotation. This would obviously include records of actual cost incurred up to the date of the quotation.

Records of actual cost incurred after the date of the quotation are not relevant to the project manager (other than in respect of correcting assumptions stated by the project manager in his instruction to the contractor to submit a quotation) as once a quotation has been accepted it is not changed even if the forecast is shown to have been incorrect.

If the contractor does not submit a quotation the project manager makes the assessment. However, the project manager will find it difficult to do so in the absence of records and details that would ordinarily only be available to the contractor.

Main options C, D, E and F require the contractor to keep records of accounts of payments of defined cost, proof that the payments have been made, communications about and assessments of compensation events for subcontractors and other records as stated in the works information. The contractor is required to allow the project manager to inspect at any time within working hours the accounts and records which he is required to keep. There is no similar provision for main options A and B.

Frequently asked questions

Q. If the contractor makes a mistake in his tender is he bound to that price for future compensation events?

A. No. Compensation events are assessed using defined costs. Therefore mistakes in the tender are not compounded by compensation events.

Q. What can the contractor do if the project manager makes his own assessment of a compensation event with which the contractor disagrees?

A. The contractor can ask the project manager to change his decision. If the project manager refuses to do so the contractor can refer the project manager's assessment to an adjudicator who has the power to review and revise the action of the project manager.

Q. Can the contractor object to an instruction from the project manager requiring the contractor to submit a quotation?

A. No. However, if the contractor believes that the effects of a compensation event are too uncertain to be forecast reasonably he can ask the project manager to revise his instruction so as to state assumptions about the event. If the project manager refuses to do so and subsequently makes his own assessment of the compensation event the contractor can refer the matter to an adjudicator who has the power to review and revise any action of the project manager.

8

Payment, withholding and the right to suspend under HGCRA 1996

A copy of the relevant provisions of HGCRA 1996 and the Scheme for Construction Contracts is contained in Appendices 1–4 of this book.

Introduction

Since 1 May 1998, and the coming into force of HGCRA 1996, no discussion of basic payment mechanisms in construction would be complete without reference to the compulsory payment regime instituted by HGCRA 1996. Section 104 of HGCRA 1996 provides an extensive definition of 'construction contracts' and, at base, that definition refers back to a contract for the carrying out of 'construction operations', which are then defined in more detail in s. 105.

Whereas the provisions of the Act regarding adjudication were perhaps the most innovative, introducing a completely new method of dispute resolution for the construction industry quite unlike any procedures that had previously been available, the provisions regarding payment were at least as controversial. The Act sought to impose terms for payment on commercial contracts regardless of whether or not the parties were of equal or unequal bargaining power. This was not an attempt to protect the small business from the large who might have been abusing its commercial dominance by insisting on unreasonably favourable payment terms. The relative size of the parties is completely irrelevant. There will be many occasions where the benefit of the Act is given to the large subcontractor in dealing with the small main contractor, or the very large construction company carrying out work for the relatively small client.

The provisions of the Act with regard to payment apply in the same circumstances as the provisions regarding adjudication. It is therefore necessary to consider whether the relevant contract is for 'construction operations' and whether it is a 'construction contract', as per the terms defined in s. 104 and 105 of the Act. The payment provisions do not apply to contracts excluded from the operation of Part II of the Act (s. 106), and only apply to contracts that are agreements in writing (s. 107).

The payment provisions differ from those relating to adjudication in the way in which they are incorporated into the contract. The contract is required to comply with the requirements of the Act regarding adjudication. If it does not comply with all the requirements, the adjudication provisions of the Scheme for Construction Contracts apply to the contract. The contract may contain an adjudication procedure which complies with some but not all of the Act's requirements. Nevertheless, the Scheme's adjudication procedures will be imposed and will replace any contractual provision that is in conflict with the Scheme.

This is not the case with the provisions as to payment. Any contractual provision which complies with the Act will remain effective, and the Scheme will only operate to replace non-compliant provisions or to fill a gap where no provision is made at all.

There are also some provisions of the Act relating to withholding payment, suspension of performance, and conditional payment provisions, which are mandatory regardless of the terms of the contract. They do not rely for their application on the implication of terms into the contract.

The limits of HGCRA 1996

Many construction contracts will fall within the ambit of HGCRA 1996. However, there is a broad class of contracts which are specifically excluded from the implications of the Act. These are set out at s. 105(2) and include:

(a) drilling for, or extraction of oil or natural gas;
(b) extraction of minerals or tunnelling or boring of construction of underground works, for this purpose;

(c)   assembly and installation, demolition of plant and machinery, or erection or demolition of steelworks for the purposes of supporting or providing access to plant and machinery on a site where the primary activity is;
- nuclear processing, power generation or water or effluent treatment; or
- the production, transmission, processing or bulk storage (other than warehousing) of chemicals, pharmaceuticals, oil, gas, steel, food and drink;

(d)   manufacture and delivery to a site of building or engineering components or equipment, materials, plant or machinery or components for systems for heating, lighting, air-conditioning, ventilation, sanitation, water supply or fire protection and for security or communication systems except under a contract which also provides their installation; and

(e)   the making, installation and repair of artistic works, being sculptures, murals and other works which are wholly artistic in nature.

In addition the Secretary of State has exercised his devolved powers to specifically exclude PFI agreements and development agreements, i.e. where the contract also includes for provisional grant or disposal of an interest in land from the Act.

There are also other contracts to which the Act does not apply such as:

1   where the construction operations are carried out outside England, Wales or Scotland (s. 104(6)(b));
2   construction contracts with a residential occupier (s. 106); or
3   construction contracts where not all of the terms have been recorded in writing, for example where some of the terms have been agreed orally or by conduct (s. 107).

As to this last requirement (that all of the terms of the construction contracts have to be recorded in writing for the Act to apply) there is currently (September 2008) a draft bill before Parliament which proposes to repeal that provision.

The right to stage payments

Section 109 of HGCRA 1996 provides that:

'(1)   A party to a construction contract is entitled to payment by instalments, stage payments or other periodic payments for any work under the contract unless–
    '(a)   it is specified in the contract that the duration of the work is to be less than 45 days, or
    '(b)   it is agreed between the parties that the duration of the work is estimated to be less than 45 days.

(2)   The parties are free to agree the amounts of the payments and the intervals at which, or circumstances in which, they become due.

(3)   In the absence of such agreement, the relevant provisions of the Scheme for Construction Contracts apply.

(4)   References in the following sections to a payment under the contract include a payment by virtue of this section.'

Most forms of contract in the construction industry, whether standard forms or custom drafted, include provisions for payments on account as the work progresses, and many will have assumed that where nothing specific is stated, any contract for work lasting longer than say a couple of months would have an implied entitlement to periodic payments. It was by no means established, however, that this was the case, and at best it could be said that in some circumstances a term might be implied to that effect. Section 109 has therefore made the position much clearer.

Where HGCRA 1996 applies to the contract, the right to some form of periodic payment is absolute unless the contract specifies that the duration of the work is to be less than 45 days or the parties agree that it is estimated to be less than 45 days. Clearly therefore if it is a term of the contract that the work will be complete in a shorter period, there will be no right to an interim payment unless the contract states otherwise. The agreement to an estimated time of less than 45 days may be much less clear. The agreement need not necessarily be contained in the contract itself. It is even possible that the contract period, stated in the contract, will be for a longer period, but the parties may agree orally that notwithstanding the obligation to complete in such longer period, it is likely that the works will be complete more quickly. This agreement might be made before or after works have started, although it is perhaps unlikely that a party will voluntarily give up a right to interim payment after work has started by agreeing that the duration is likely to be less than 45 days.

The meaning of 'duration' is not entirely clear. If work is to be carried out in two site visits, each lasting ten days, over a period of two months, there may be an argument that the duration of the work is in fact 20 days. Alternatively it may be said that the duration is 60 days. It is submitted, but without any authority, that the latter is probably the correct interpretation.

It is also unclear what the difference is between 'instalments, stage payments or other periodic payments'. It is possible that the three terms, which might all mean the same thing, were included in order to make it clear that any contractual provision is acceptable, so long as it involves payment on some basis other than one payment at the end of the job. In this, and in what follows in s. 110(2), the maximum flexibility is allowed to contracting parties to make arrangements that suit their circumstances.

Whether the Act applies or not the parties are free to agree how much is to be paid and when. The most onerous payment terms might be included and still satisfy the Act's requirements. For example, in a contract for work to a value of £1m to be carried out over six months, it might be agreed that there will be one payment of £500 after five months, and the balance paid at the end (or substantially later than the end) of the job. Such terms have not been common before the Act and there is no reason why they should become popular now, but they are perfectly compatible with the Act. The important point is that the Act allows maximum flexibility in payment arrangements. If, however, the question of interim payments is not addressed at the time of the contract, the Scheme will apply and will impose its regime.

The Scheme deals with the timing of periodic payments and the quantification of them together. The Scheme's provisions are considered below.

If HGCRA 1996 applies but the contractual payment mechanisms are either non-compliant or absent then the Scheme for Construction Contracts will apply. The first calculation required is the value of work. 'Work' is defined in para. 12 and 'any work or services mentioned in section 104 of the Act'. It includes only construction operations and services relating to such operations. Accordingly, if the contract also covers other matters, the stage payments calculated and payable under the Scheme will not include such other matters.

'Value of work' is defined in para. 12 of the Scheme as:

> '... an amount determined in accordance with the construction contract under which the work is performed or where the contract contains no such provision, the cost of any work performed in accordance with that contract together with an amount equal to any overhead or profit included in the contract price.'

If the contract contains any method of valuing the work, that method will be used to calculate the stage payment, but if the contract does not contain any such method, the payment is calculated on the basis of the cost of the work plus overheads and profit. Therefore, it is important that a method should be established clearly in the contract if the parties wish to avoid interim payments being calculated on a 'cost plus' basis. There is a protection in subpara. (4) against the contract price being exceeded by the use of the cost plus method of valuation, but a stage payment valued on this basis may be substantially different from the proper proportion of the contract price.

This first stage of calculation requires the evaluation of the work from the start of the contract to 'the end of the relevant period'. That term is defined in para. 12 as:

> '... a period which is specified in, or is calculated by reference to the construction contract or where no such period is so specified or is so calculable, a period of 28 days.'

If then the contract specifies that stage payments shall be payable every three months, that is the period that will be used for the calculation under the Scheme. There is no requirement for any particular period to be agreed, and any agreement will be respected by the Scheme. If, however, there is no agreement, stage payments will be every 28 days. The calculation does not require consideration just of the work carried out since the last valuation. The total value to date is calculated.

Having calculated 'the value of work', the next stage is to calculate the value of materials, providing that the contract provides for payment for materials. Materials that have already been incorporated in the work will have been valued under the preceding paragraph. If there is no contractual entitlement to payment in respect of materials not yet incorporated, they will not be valued under this paragraph. There is no entitlement under this paragraph to payment for off-site materials. There is no definition of value of materials, and it is not clear whether the 'cost plus' basis that is the default method for valuing work applies. Once again, the valuation is to cover the whole period from commencement.

Finally there is sweep-up paragraph, requiring the addition of any other sum payable under the contract. This would include any express entitlement to payment in respect of off-site materials, one-off design fees, etc.

Having calculated the total payable under the contract to date, the calculation then requires the subtraction of all sums that have been paid or have become due for payment from the start of the contract up to the end of the relevant period; the sum now being calculated has not of course yet become payable. The subtraction gives the net sum payable in respect of the relevant period.

There is then a safeguard against overpayment. The amount of a stage payment can never exceed the 'contract price', which is defined in para. 12 as 'the entire sum payable under the construction contract in respect of the work'. If, therefore, there has been a series of calculations based on cost plus overhead and profit, which apparently values the work at rather more than the contract price, there is a cap preventing the contractor from being paid the excess. 'Contract price' does not necessarily mean the sum that was agreed at the start – it includes the price of variations, and allowances for fluctuations and the like.

Dates for payment

The Act deals with two important dates: the date when a payment becomes due and the final date for payment. The Scheme has to deal with both, and where a contract is to

133

include stage payments (i.e. a contract expected to last more than 45 days) there has to be provision both for stage payments and the final payment.

Paragraphs 3 to 7 of the Scheme deal with the dates on which payments become due:

'(3)   Where the parties to a construction contract fail to provide adequate mechanism for determining either what payments become due under the contract, or when they become due for payment, or both, the relevant provisions of paragraphs 4 to 7 shall apply.

(4)   Any payment of a kind mentioned in paragraph 2 above shall become due on whichever of the following dates occurs later –

   (a)   the expiry of 7 days following the relevant period mentioned in paragraph 2(1) above, or

   (b)   the making of a claim by the payee.

(5)   The final payment under a relevant construction contract namely the payment of an amount equal to the difference (if any) between –

   (a)   the contract price, and

   (b)   the aggregate of any instalment or stage or periodic payments which have become due under the contract,

   shall become due on the expiry of

   (a)   30 days following completion of the work, or

   (b)   the making of a claim by the payee,

   whichever is the later.

(6)   Payment of the contract price under a construction contract (not being a relevant construction contract) shall become due on –

   (a)   the expiry of 30 days following the completion of the work, or

   (b)   the making of claims by the payee,

   whichever is the later.

(7)   Any other payment under a construction contract shall become due –

   (a)   on the expiry of 7 days following the completion of the work to which the payment relates, or

   (b)   the making of a claim by the payee,

   whichever is the later.'

Once again it must be remembered that these provisions are only relevant if the contract comes within the Act but fails to provide an adequate payment mechanism. Under the Act the parties are free to agree any terms they like to cover what payments are to become due and when they are to become due, subject only to the overriding requirement in a contract for 45 days or more for there to be stage payments of some sort. These paragraphs can only come into effect if the parties failed to do that.

Paragraph 4 deals with stage payments. It does not apply either to the final payment in a contract where there have been stage payments, nor does it apply to a contract which is not required to provide for stage payments because it was not anticipated that the work would last for 45 days or more. The stage payments will become due seven days after the expiry of each relevant period, discussed above, or on the making of a claim by the payee, whichever is the later.

It is therefore necessary first to consider when the relevant period expires. The contract may establish this. If it does not, then the first relevant period will expire 28 days after commencement of the contract. This does not necessarily mean commencement of work on site. If the work is the execution of groundworks, commencement probably will be the day that the contractor first goes to the site, but if the work includes design services the commencement will be the start of the performance of those services.

On the expiry of the first relevant period the second relevant period starts. This will be the case even if work is not continuous. There may well be gaps during which no work is carried out at all. Nevertheless relevant periods will continue to tick by.

The stage payment does not necessarily become due at the end of the relevant period, although the contract may provide that it does. If the contract is silent on the point, the stage payment will become due seven days later, or on the making of a claim by a payee. The later of these two dates is the date that payment becomes due. If, therefore, seven days pass without any claim being made by the payee, no payment is due until the claim is made. If the claim is presented within the seven-day period, the stage payment becomes due at the end of that period. 'Claim by payee' is defined in para. 12, and if the payee submits an application that does not satisfy the requirements of the definition the stage payment will not become due. The definition reads thus:

> '... a written notice given by the party carrying out work under a construction contract to the other party specifying the amount of any payment or payments which he considers to be due and the basis on which it is, or they are calculated.'

A simple statement that a figure is due will not be sufficient. The basis of calculation must be given. There is, however, no requirement that the claim should be correct. A claim for a wildly exaggerated sum, with a clearly incorrect calculation, will be enough to ensure that a payment becomes due. The payment that becomes due will not be the sum for which application has been made, but the date that it becomes due will be established. It is clearly important to any prospective payee that a claim for payment is submitted as soon as possible after the end of the relevant period, or even perhaps a day or two before. This will ensure that the payment becomes due at the expiry of the seven days.

The final payment (not to be confused with the 'final date for payment' which will be considered later) under a contract that has had stage payments is dealt with by para. 5 of Part II of the Scheme. The final payment is the total of the contract price, computed to take account of all omissions, additions and other sums due from one party to the other under the contract, less all the stage payments that have become due during the course of the work. It becomes due, subject of course to other provisions of the contract, 30 days after completion of the work or on the making of a claim by the payee, whichever is the later. There is no allowance made here for the sophistication of practical completion, defects periods, retention, certification of making good and the like. If parties wish to provide for such things they must include express conditions in their contracts. Whether or not the work is complete, and when completion was achieved, will continue to be major sources of dispute.

Contracts that specify that the duration of the work will be less than 45 days or where the parties have agreed that the duration is estimated to be less than 45 days, are not subject to the requirement for stage payments, and unless the contract provides for interim payments there is no entitlement to payment until the end of the work. Paragraph 6 covers these contracts. The single payment is due 30 days after the completion of the work, or on the making of a claim by the payee, whichever is the later. The claim by the payee is subject to the same requirements as those discussed above.

Paragraph 7 sweeps up any payments that have not been caught by the previous paragraphs. Any such entitlement will be treated in the same way as a stage payment and will become due seven days after the completion of the work to which it relates or on the making of a claim, whichever is the later.

Final date for payment

The final date for payment is significant as the last date when the payee can expect to receive payment, the date on which the payee can give notice of intention to suspend performance and as the basis for establishing the latest date for the payer to give a notice of intention to withhold all or part of the payment. Paragraph 8 deals with a position where no final date for payment has been agreed:

'(1)   Where the parties to a construction contract fail to provide a final date for payment in relation to any sum which becomes due under a construction contract, the provisions of this paragraph shall apply.

(2)   The final date for the making of any payment of a kind mentioned in paragraphs 2, 5, 6, or 7 shall be 17 days from the date that payment becomes due.'

This is a simple statement. The final date for payment is 17 days after the payment becomes due and is not directly related to the valuation date or the end of the relevant period. If the payee has delayed putting in a claim for payment, so that the 'payment due' date is later than seven days after the end of the period, the final date for payment will also be extended.

Timing and quantification of payments

Section 110 of HGCRA 1996 provides that:

'(1)   Every construction contract shall–
    (a)   provide an adequate mechanism for determining what payments become due under the contract, and when, and

         (b)   provide for a final date for payment in relation to any sum which becomes due.

               The parties are free to agree how long the period is to be between the date on which a sum becomes due and the final date for payment.

(2)   ...

(3)   If or to the extent that a contract does not contain such provision as is mentioned in subsection (1) or (2), the relevant provisions of the Scheme for Construction Contracts apply.'

Once again the Act allows maximum flexibility in enabling the parties to make such arrangements for payment as they think appropriate or can negotiate. Any 'mechanism' can be stipulated – the only requirement is that it should be 'effective'. The parties must be able to work out how much is due and when it is due. Payments may be calculated on a straight line basis, on the basis of the value of work carried out, stages reached in the construction process, or on any other basis, so long as the terms are agreed at the time that the contract is made.

There is, as yet, no judicial comment on what does or does not constitute an adequate mechanism, perhaps because an adjudicator's decision on the point is unlikely to be susceptible to challenge in summary proceedings. It is suggested that the words should be given their normal common-sense meaning. A contract can certainly have a mechanism for such matters which is inadequate. One example can be found in the facts that lay behind the first reported decision involving the Act, *Macob Civil Engineering Ltd v Morrison Construction Ltd* (1999) 64 Con LR 1 (Mr Justice Dyson). The subcontract between the parties had contained conflicting terms as to the dates for payment in the several subcontract documents. Having heard evidence on the point, the adjudicator had decided that he could not establish what the terms for payment were, if indeed any had been agreed at all. He concluded that there was therefore no adequate mechanism in place, and that the Scheme's provisions should apply.

Subcontractors sometimes argue that a clause in their subcontracts linking payment of retention to certification under the main contract, which may of course be delayed by circumstances for which the subcontractor has no responsibility whatsoever, is not an adequate mechanism for establishing when payment of retention is to be made. This will be considered further when dealing with conditional payments or 'pay-when-paid' clauses.

Time for payment must be dealt with in two stages. The first, under s. 110(1)(a), is the time at which a payment becomes due. This is the date at which the entitlement to payment crystallises, but it is not the date at which it is to be paid. That involves a second stage, required under s. 110(1)(b). At some stage after the payment becomes due, the final date for payment will be reached. This is the end of the 'credit period' and payment must be made no later than that date. Each sum due, whether an interim or final payment, will have a final date for payment. The concept is important. The final date for payment enables a date to be established as the last date for giving notice of intention to withhold payment. Failure to pay by that date can also provide the contractor with a right to suspend performance.

The Act does not impose any credit period on the parties. They are free to agree any period at all. Once again though the object of the Act is to ensure that the parties do agree something so that there is no argument about when money should be paid.

If the parties fail to agree a method of establishing how much is to be paid, when a payment is due or a final date for payment, the Scheme will supplement their contract to achieve clarity.

Section 109(1) states that a 'party to a construction contract is entitled to payment by instalments, stage payments or other periodic payments for any work done under the contract' except where the work was to be less than 45 days.

Section 110(1) provides that construction contracts shall provide adequate mechanisms for determining what payments become due under the contract and when and also provide for a final date for payment in relation to any sums which become due.

Frequently asked questions

Q. Do the HGCRA 1996 payment provisions apply to all construction contracts?

A. No. There are a lot of construction contracts that fall outside the scope of the HGCRA 1996. For example, the Act does not encompass construction contracts with residential occupiers, erection of plant in many process type industries, or contracts that are not wholly recorded in writing, or contracts for construction operations outside of the UK. However, the provisions of the Act are currently under review and in particular the requirements that construction contracts must be wholly recorded in writing for the provisions of the Act to apply are likely to be repealed.

Q. Does the HGCRA 1996 require clients to make regular interim payments?

A. No. Where HGCRA 1996 applies and where the construction period is longer than 45 days the Act only requires that some provision for interim payments is made. This does not require regular payments. For example, one payment at the beginning and one payment at the end will be sufficient. In the absence of any such provisions the Scheme for Construction Contracts will apply, which requires payments to be made at intervals of 28 days.

Q. What are the consequences of failing to issue a payment notice (a section 110 notice) within the stipulated time?

A. Subject to any contractual provisions to the contrary (see, e.g., JCT Design and Build Contract) there are no consequences of failing to issue a section 110 notice. Even if the payment notice is never issued the paying party will not be obliged to pay more than the works are worth. See *SL Timber Systems v Carillion Construction Ltd* [2001] BLR 516 below.

Q. What are the consequences of failing to issue a withholding notice (a section 111 notice) within the stipulated time?

A. Provided that the Act applies to the contract in question failure to issue a withholding notice within the stipulated period will generally prevent the paying party from withholding any sums from the amount that would otherwise be due. However, this general proposition is qualified by the judgment of the House of Lords in *Melville Dundas (in Receivership) v George Wimpey UK Ltd* [2007] UKHL 18 in which it was held that where a contractual right to withhold payment arises after the final date for issuing the notice but before payment is made the paying party may be entitled to rely on that contractual right notwithstanding that the withholding notice would be out of time.

Section 110 and section 111 notices

Section 110(2) requires the payer to give notice to the payee not later than five days after the date on which payment becomes due from him under the contract or would have become due if:

'(a)   the other party had carried out his obligations under the contract; and
(b)   no set-off for abatement was permitted by reference to any sum claimed to be due under one or more other contracts'

This is referred to as a payment notice. The Act goes on to state that 'if or to the extent that a contract does not contain such provision as is mentioned in subsection (1) or (2), the relevant provisions of the Scheme for Construction Contracts (the "Scheme") apply'.

In general simple terms the Scheme requires the following:

- not later than five days after the date that the amount becomes due the payer is to give a payment notice specifying the amount of the proposed payment and the basis on which it is calculated;
- the final date for payment is 17 days from the date that the amount becomes due;
- no later than five days before the final date for payment, the payer may give notice specifying the amount to be deducted or withheld from the amount due and the grounds for such deduction/withholding; and
- if the payer fails to pay by the final date for payment and the failure continues for seven days after the payee has given notice of intention to suspend his performance the payee may suspend the performance.

The contract must provide for the giving of such notice, and if it does not, the Scheme will fill the gap. The maximum period of five days has nothing to do with the final date for payment which may be some time off. It may be that there is in fact nothing to pay because the payee has not performed, or the payer may have a valid right of set-off or abatement in respect of matters arising under other contracts. Nevertheless the payer should still give notice.

It is not sufficient for the contract to require the payer to state the sum that he is going to pay. The basis of the calculation must be shown as well. If the value of the work is subject to some abatement because of defect, this should be made clear. The calculation that is required may involve a summary of the valuation of the works, a deduction by way of abatement, deduction of retention and discount and of course the sum of previous payments made. It should also deal with VAT. The important question is: how much is going to be paid and how has it been calculated? On receipt of the notice, the payee should be entirely clear about the position. If the contract does not provide for this, the Scheme will do so.

This process is something like a traditional certification, but the 'certificate' is not given by a quasi-independent third party, such as the engineer or the architect, but by the paying party himself. It is to be given not more than five days after the payment became due, which as we have seen may not be until the payee has made a claim setting out in some detail what he believes he is entitled to be paid.

The intention is of course that the payer should give sufficient information to enable the payee to understand exactly what he is being paid and why, so that if he considers that he is not being paid his proper entitlement he can raise the issue at a comparatively early stage. Hopefully that matter can be resolved by discussion, but if necessary adjudication is available without any serious delay. It is curious that this intention is not supported by any sanction for failure to give a notice in accordance with this paragraph. There is nothing in the Scheme that provides for anything to happen if the payer gives no notice at all, let alone a notice that is not fully detailed.

This was not the original intention of the draftsmen of the Scheme. In early drafts it was suggested that the payee would present his application for payment, and unless the payer countered the application with a detailed statement of what he thought was the appropriate amount and why, the payee's application would be conclusive of the amount that would have to be paid, subject of course to the right of set-off on giving notice as required by s. 111. This proposal was well publicised, for example, in the consultation paper *Making the Scheme for*

Construction Contracts, and it was widely expected that this would be the position in all contracts to which the scheme applied.

This original intention was abandoned, but it is commonly argued in adjudication proceedings that if the payer has failed to give a notice specifying the payment that he intends to make, the claim made by the payee should be taken as being conclusive as to the sum that should be paid as a stage payment. Specific terms of the contract may give this argument a proper basis (as, for example, in the JCT Design and Build Contract) but there is nothing in the Scheme to support it. Nevertheless, uncertainty on this point is widespread, particularly in view of the very clear sanction for failure to give notice of intention to withhold under s. 111 of the Act and para. 10 of Part II of the Scheme. Discussion of the point continues in the next section.

Withholding payment

Section 111 of HGCRA 1996 requires a second notice to be given if the payer intends to withhold some or all of the payment that has fallen due:

'(1) A party to a construction contract may not withhold payment after the final date for payment of a sum due under the contract unless he has given an effective notice of intention to withhold payment.
The notice mentioned in section 110(2) may suffice as a notice of intention to withhold payment if it complies with the requirements of this section.

(2) To be effective such a notice must specify –
(a) the amount proposed to be withheld and the ground for withholding payment, or
(b) if there is more than one ground, each ground and the amount attributable to it,
and must be given not later than the prescribed period before the final date for payment.

(3) The parties are free to agree what the prescribed period is to be.
In the absence of such agreement, the period shall be that provided by the Scheme for Construction Contracts.

> (4)   Where an effective notice of intention to withhold payment is given, but on the matter being referred to adjudication it is decided that the whole or part of the amount should be paid, the decision shall be construed as requiring payment not later than –
> (i)   seven days from the date of the decision, or
> (ii)   the date which apart from the notice would have been the final date for payment,
> whichever is the later.'

Unlike the requirement for a notice to be given of the amount that is to be paid (under s. 110) the requirement for a notice of intention to withhold does not depend on the construction contract. The parties are not required to include such a term in their contract. The Scheme for Construction Contracts is not invoked in order to fill in the gap if the requirement is not included in the contract. Whatever the contract says, a party to a construction contract may not withhold a payment that has become due unless an effective notice of intention to withhold has been given.

The notice given under s. 110(2) may be effective as a notice of withholding under s. 111, so long as the other requirements of s. 111 are satisfied. This notice should have been given within five days of the money becoming due, by which time the ground(s) for withholding payment may have been clear. Notice of intention to withhold does not need to be given that early unless the parties have included a term to that effect in their contract. It is quite likely that the reason for wishing to withhold all or part of the payment will not have been apparent at the time of the earlier notice.

The requirements of the notice are simply that the amount to be withheld is stated and the ground or grounds given. If there is more than one ground, each should be stated with the amount relating to it. The contract may impose further requirements, although as it will probably have been drafted by the paying party it is unlikely to do so.

The notice must be given not later than the prescribed period before the final date for payment. The final date for payment is a date that is either established by the express words of the contract as required by s. 110(1), or alternatively has been imposed on the contract in default by the Scheme.

There is no requirement for any minimum or maximum period of notice. The parties can, if they wish, decide to require notice of intention to withhold payment to be given 28 days before the final date for payment. Similarly, the period, if agreed in the contract, can be as little as one day. The important point is that the parties should have addressed the issue and decided what the period should be. If that point is not covered in the contract the Scheme provides:

> '10. Any notice of intention to withhold payment mentioned in section 111 of the Act shall be given not later than the prescribed period, which is to say not later than 7 days before the final date for payment determined either in accordance with the construction contract, or where no such provision is made in the contract, in accordance with paragraph 8 above.'

The notice must be given not less than seven days before the final date for payment, which itself is established either by the contract or in default by para. 8 of Part II of the Scheme.

If the payer has not given notice of intention to withhold in due time he will not be able to withhold the payment or any part of it. This clear sanction for failure to give a notice required by the Act is in stark contrast to the absence of any sanction for failure to give the notice of the amount of the proposed payment within five days from the date the payment became due.

The judgment of Judge Bowsher QC in *Northern Developments (Cumbria) Ltd v J&J Nichol* [2000] BLR 158 has led to some confusion on this point. He reviewed the statutory provisions regarding payment and came to this conclusion:

> 'The act by section 111 imposes on the parties a direct requirement that the paying party may not withhold a payment after the due date for payment unless he has given an effective notice of intention to withhold payment. That seems to me to have a direct bearing on the ambit of any dispute to be heard by an adjudicator. Section 110 requires that the contract must require that within 5 days of any sum falling due under the contract, the paying party must give a statement of the amount due or of what would be due if the payee had performed the contract. Section 111 provides that no deduction can be made after the final date for payment unless the paying party has given notice of intention to withhold

> payment. The intention of the statute is clearly that if there is to be a dispute about the amount of the payment required by section 111, that dispute is to be mentioned in a notice of intention to withhold payment not later than 5 days after the due date for payment . . . For the temporary striking of balances which are contemplated by the Act, there is to be no dispute about any matter not raised in the notice of intention to withhold payment.'

With respect to the learned judge, there are several points within the passage set out above which are misleading. First, s. 110 does not require, 'that the contract must require that within five days of any sum falling due under the contract, the paying party must give a statement of the amount due or of what would be due if the payee had performed the contract'. The section deals with the timing of the notice. The notice is to be given no later than five days after the date on which the payment becomes due, *or would have become due if the other had carried out its obligations,* etc. There is no need to state what amount would have become due if the payee had performed.

There is then a suggestion that if there is any dispute about the amount to be paid, the dispute is to be mentioned in a notice of intention to withhold given not later than five days after the due date for payment. There are many potential disputes that will not be mentioned in a notice of intention to withhold. A dispute about the value of work done will not be covered by any notice of intention to withhold. If the first of the two statements has been given, there may well be a clear dispute on the valuation, but as has been stressed above there is no sanction for failure to give that notice.

Furthermore, a notice of intention to withhold need not be given as early as five days after the due date for payment. If the Scheme is operating in all respects, the contract having completely failed to provide any of the Act's requirements, the final date for payment is 17 days after the payment due date, and the latest date for notice of intention to withhold is seven days before that, or ten days after the payment due date.

In fact in the *Northern Developments* case, the adjudicator had correctly interpreted the position on this point. In a letter to the parties he had said:

'As for lack of notices pursuant to section 110(2) of the Act, I considered that as the Scheme is silent as to the consequences of failure to comply and furthermore as the value of the works had to be that properly carried out, then as stated previously, I decided that the question of defects and their value could be dealt with by me.'

If an adjudicator, or indeed a judge or arbitrator, is asked to decide how much is properly payable he must go back to first principles and enquire into the value of the works, established in accordance with the contract.

Judge Bowsher revisited the question of valuation and the relationship between s. 110 and 111 of the Act in *Whiteways Contractors v Impresa Castelli Construction* (2000) 75 Con LR 92:

'Of course, in considering a dispute, an adjudicator will make his own valuation of the claim before him and in doing so, he may abate the claim in respects not mentioned in the notice of intention to withhold payment. But he ought not to look into abatements outside the four corners of the claim unless they have been mentioned in a notice of intention to withhold payment. So, to take a hypothetical example, if there is dispute about valuation 10, the adjudicator may make his own valuation of the matters referred to in valuation 10 whether or not they are referred to him specifically in a notice of intention to withhold payment. But it would be wrong for him to enquire into an alleged overvaluation on valuation 6, whether the paying party alleges abatement or set-off, unless the notice of intention to withhold payment identified that as a matter of dispute.'

If the dispute is about valuation 10, then a claim that valuation 6 was overvalued and a credit is due back is in reality a claim for a set-off, not a claim for an abatement.

Failure to issue notices

Initially a substantial amount of case law developed around the notice of intention to withhold payment and the failure to issue a section 110 payment notice.

Three issues were contentious but now appear to be settled law.

1 There is no sanction for failure to issue a section 110 notice.
2 If no withholding notice has been issued the defence of set-off cannot be used except in exceptional circumstances.
3 A defence can be raised that the sum claimed was not due to be paid under the contract and therefore no withholding notice was required even after the final date for payment has passed.

Perhaps the clearest illustration of the approval taken by the courts is the decision of the Court of Appeal in *Rupert Morgan Building Services (LLC) Ltd v Jervis* [2003] EWCA Civ 1563. The defendants claimed to be able to raise certain defences for non-payment which did not require a withholding notice. Those defences were: (i) work that had not been done, (ii) duplication of items, (iii) claimed extras within the contract, and (iv) claimed work was a correction of defects. The Court of Appeal found, on the terms of the contract, that it was not the actual work done which defined the 'sum due' for the purposes of s. 111 of the Act, but simply the amount identified in the interim certificate. Without a withholding notice, the sum identified in the certificate would have to be paid.

In *SL Timber Systems v Carillion Construction Ltd* [2001] BLR 516, Court of Sessions, Lord Macfadyen concluded that the absence of a withholding notice or a notice under s. 110(2) of intention to deduct does not relieve a party from making a claim from the ordinary burden of showing that he is entitled under the contract to receive the payment he claims.

The House of Lords decision in *Melville Dundas (in Receivership) v George Wimpey UK Ltd* [2007] UKHL 18 is one that has caused some surprise in the construction industry and would appear to present the possibility of quite significant circumvention of the notice provisions within s. 109, 110 and 111 of HGCRA 1996.

Melville Dundas (MD) were employed by Wimpey. The contract was in the JCT Standard Form with Contractors' Design, 1998 edition. On 2 May 2003, MD applied for an interim payment of £396,630. It was accepted that sum was due and that the final date for payment was 16 May 2003. Wimpey did not pay. On 22 May 2003, MD went into receivership. They had very substantial debts. The receivers claimed payment of the sum of £396,630 and Wimpey relied on clause 27.6.5.1 of the contract which provided:

'Subject to clauses 27.5.3 and 27.6.5.2 the provisions of this contract which require any further payment or any release or further release of retention to the contractor shall not apply; provided that clause 27.6.5.1 shall not be construed so as to prevent the enforcement by the contractor of any rights under this contract in respect of amounts properly due to be paid by the employer to the contractor which the employer has unreasonably not paid and which, where clause 27.3.4 applies, have accrued 28 days or more before the date when under clause 27.3.4 the employer could first give notice to determine the employment of the contractor ...'

MD contended that these contractual provisions were contrary to s. 111(1) of HGCRA 1996 which provides that:

'A party to a construction contract may not withhold payment after the final date for payment of a sum due under the contract unless he has given an effective notice of intention to withhold payment.'

Allowing Wimpey's appeal against the decision of the Inner House, and restoring the judgment of the Lord Ordinary, the House of Lords decided (3:2) that Wimpey was entitled to withhold the payment and that there was no conflict with the provisions of HGCRA 1996 such as would preclude withholding.

Lord Hoffmann, doubting whether Parliament can have taken into account that parties might enter into contracts where a contractual ground for withholding payment might arise *after* the final date for payment, said that (para. 22):

'... section 111(1) should be construed as not applying to a lawful ground for withholding payment of which it was in the nature of things not possible for notice to have been given within the statutory time frame ...'

Lord Hope (on the relevant point) and Lord Walker agreed with the speech of Lord Hoffmann. However, Lord Neuberger (in a speech with which Lord Mance agreed) summarised the opposing view in the following way (paras 63 and 64):

'Section 110(1)(b) requires a construction contract to "provide a final date for payment in relation to any sum which becomes due". In this case, the contract complied with this requirement in relation to interim payments through the medium of clause 30.3.6. On the facts of this case, the "final date" for the payment of the sum was 16 May 2003. Section 111(1) prohibits the appellant from "withhold[ing] payment …" after "the final date for payment of a sum due under the contract". In this case, that must mean that the appellant "may not withhold payment" of the sum after 16 May 2003. Accordingly, in so far as clause 27.6.5.1 has the effect of permitting the appellant to withhold payment of the sum, it is purporting to permit that which section 111(1) prohibits. Therefore, to that extent, it is ineffective.'

The decision in *Melville Dundas* is directly relevant to the facts before His Honour Judge Peter Coulson QC in the recent decision in *Pierie Design International v Mark Johnston* [2007] EWHC 1691 (TCC). Despite arguments to the contrary, the Judge regarded himself as bound by the decision of the majority in the *Melville Dundas* case. Interestingly, however, the determination event in *Pierie Design* is not the fact of administrative receivership, as in *Melville Dundas*, but a failure to proceed regularly and diligently with the works.

Section 111 of the Act provides that a party to a construction contract may not withhold payment after the final date for payment of a sum due under the contract unless he has given an effective notice of intention to withhold payment. The notice mentioned in s. 110(2) may be sufficient if it complies with the requirement of s. 111 of the Act. The notice must specify the amount proposed to be withheld and the ground for withholding payment. If there is more than one ground, the notice must state each ground and the amount attributable to it. It must also be given not later than the prescribed period before the final date for payment. If the parties do not agree the period, para. 10 of Part II of the Scheme contains the relevant implied term. Failure to issue a notice under s. 111 of the Act does not preclude a party from arguing before an adjudicator that the sum claimed did not fall due, it merely precludes the raising of a counterclaim. A notice under s. 111 must be in writing and must be served after the relevant application for payment has been made. See *Strathmore Building Services Ltd v Colin Scott Greig t/a Hestia Fireside Design* [2000] ScotCS 133. Section 111 of the Act does not apply to payments due in consequence of an adjudicator's decision and does not entitle a court to refuse a stay which would otherwise be granted under s. 9(4) of the Arbitration Act 1996.

Although s. 111 of HGCRA 1996 deals with the form of the withholding notice, it does not place any requirement on its substance. There is no requirement that the employer has a valid claim in law. Although such matters would normally be easily resolved at adjudication, the anomaly can give rise to problems in certain circumstances.

Under the current proposals for reform of HGCRA 1996 and the draft Bill currently before Parliament if the party making payment fails to issue a section 110 notice the party receiving payment can issue the notice instead. The amount stated as due in such notice then becomes payable subject to the issue of a section 111 notice.

Reinwood Ltd v L Brown & Sons Ltd [2007] EWCA Civ 601

Reinwood contracted to build several apartments for Brown on the JCT Standard Form of Contract with Quantities, 1998 edition. The architect issued several interim payment certificates but the project was delayed. Brown issued a withholding notice, purporting to set off liquidated damages against the interim certificates. Between the notice being issued and the payments falling due, the architect issued an extension of time, annulling Brown's right to liquidated damages. Brown successfully argued in the Court of Appeal that the right had 'crystallised' with the withholding notice, which remained valid notwithstanding that its deductions no longer had a legal basis. For example a contractor may not be able to suspend performance of its works in the face of an apparently valid withholding notice for an excessive sum.

Frequently asked questions

Q. If the withholding notice is excessive in value but correct in form can the contractor suspend work for non-payment?

A. If the withholding notice is correct in form and if its issue is not an abuse of process (e.g. if the notice has been issued in the certain knowledge that it is excessive then it may well be invalid even though correct in form) then the contractor may well not be able to suspend work for non-payment even if in subsequent proceedings the amount withheld is found to be excessive. However, under the Scheme for Construction Contracts the adjudicator is given express powers to open up, revise and review any decisions taken or certificates given unless the contract states that such decisions or certificates are to be final and conclusive. In exercising his power to revise a decision or certificate the adjudicator may decide that the revision should take effect from the date of issue of the certificate thereby retrospectively validating the contractor's otherwise wrongful suspension for non-payment.

Right to suspend

The right to suspend performance of the contract for non-payment is another provision that does not rely either on the parties to include a term of the contract, or on the Scheme to do it for them. Section 112 of the Act provides:

'(1)   Where a sum due under a construction contract is not paid in full by the final date for payment and no effective notice to withhold payment has been given, the person to whom the sum is due has the right (without prejudice to any other right or remedy) to suspend performance of his obligations under the contract to the party by whom payment ought to have been made ("the party in default").

(2)   The right may not be exercised without first giving to the party in default at least seven days' notice of intention to suspend performance, stating the ground or grounds on which it is intended to suspend performance.

(3)   The right to suspend performance ceases when the party in default makes payment in full of the amount due.

(4)   Any period during which performance is suspended in pursuance of the right conferred by this section shall be disregarded in computing for the purposes of any contractual time limit the time taken, by the party exercising the right or by a third party, to complete any work directly or indirectly affected by the exercise of the right.

Where the contractual time limit is set by reference to a date rather than a period, the date shall be adjusted accordingly.'

Contractors and subcontractors who have not been paid have always been tempted to suspend work as a means of encouraging the cash to flow, but conventional legal advice prior to May 1998 was that such action was dangerous. Without an express term in the contract giving a right to suspend, it would be a breach of contract to do so. The breach of payment terms would not itself usually have justified a breach in return. Failure to pay would be unlikely to amount to a repudiation of contract entitling the contractor to rescind and would only rarely become an act of prevention.

Even if there was an express or hard-to-find implied term giving a right to suspend for non-payment, it would be necessary to establish that a payment was due. Without a clear means of establishing whether a payment was in fact due, and with the possibility that unexpected contra charges might be raised, this test could be difficult. The HGCRA 1996 has now introduced into all construction contracts the right to suspend. Furthermore, the other provisions of the Act should operate to make it much clearer whether or not a payment is due. Contra charges cannot be brought into the account by surprise, as there can be no withholding of a payment unless a proper notice has been given under s. 111. If the term required by s. 110 has been complied with, the sum to which the payee is entitled should also be clear well in advance of the final date for payment.

Section 112 has certainly made suspension a much less dangerous route to follow, but there are still serious difficulties. The right to suspend cannot be exercised without giving at least seven days' notice of intention to suspend. This may be a very expensive period, and the contractor will be obliged to continue his work. If he chooses to reduce resources during that period he may find that payment is made at the end of the seven days but he has dropped several days behind programme. There will be no extension of time, and he will have to accelerate or face the consequences of being late. On the other hand he may have serious doubts that he is going to be paid at all, and not want to increase his exposure.

Once suspension has started, the contractor has some relief from the programme consequences. Section 112(4) effectively gives the contractor an entitlement to an extension of time for the period of the suspension. But there is no entitlement to further time for remobilisation of resources in order to return to site and restart. Moreover there is no statutory right to payment of the cost that has been incurred in leaving site, redeploying or laying off resources and then returning.

The rather limited right of suspension may be enlarged by specific provisions in the contract. The fact that there is a statutory right to suspend after giving seven days' notice does not prevent the parties from agreeing that there should be a contractual right to suspend with less notice. The parties might also agree that there should be an entitlement to an extension of time to cover remobilisation, and perhaps a payment of loss and expense (or similar) incurred in the suspension and remobilisation exercise. These two last points have been taken up by the JCT in the 1998 and 2005 editions of the standard forms of contract. They are, however, private contractual matters and not statutory rights.

It may also be possible for a contractor to argue that non-payment is a breach of contract, and that it must have been within the contemplation of the defaulting employer that the contractor would exercise his statutory right to suspend. The expense of suspension and remobilisation might then be claimed as damages arising out of the breach.

Section 112 of HGCRA 1996 which includes an express right to suspend for non-payment provides as follows:

'Right to suspend performance for non-payment

'(1) Where a sum due under a construction contract is not paid in full by the final date for payment and no effective notice to withhold payment has been given, the person to whom the sum is due has the right (without prejudice to any other right or remedy) to suspend performance of his obligations under the contract to the party by whom payment ought to have been made ("the party in default").

(2) The right may not be exercised without first giving to the party in default at least seven days' notice of intention to suspend performance, stating the ground or grounds on which it is intended to suspend performance.

(3) The right to suspend performance ceases when the party in default makes payment in full of the amount due.

(4) Any period during which performance is suspended in pursuance of the right conferred by the section shall be disregarded in computing for the purposes of any contractual time limit the time taken, by the party exercising the right or by

a third party, to complete any work directly or indirectly affected by the exercise of the right.

Where the contractual time limit is set by reference to a date rather than a period, the date shall be adjusted accordingly.'

The statutory provisions need to be considered with care and the steps identified need to be closely observed, so that:

- the final date for payment must have passed;
- there must be no effective notice to withhold payment. Great care will again be required to establish that any purported notice which *does* exist, is in actual fact invalid or ineffective, either because of its timing or its content;
- the right to suspend conferred under s. 112(1) may not be exercised without the party proposing to suspend first giving the party in default *at least seven days notice* of the intention to suspend performance. The notice must state the ground or grounds on which it is intended to suspend performance.

For the purpose of s. 112(1) and (2), as with other parts of HGCRA 1996, the rules in relation to the reckoning of time may be critical. The provisions of s. 116 of HGCRA 1996 ought to be consulted, and closely followed.

In the draft Bill currently before Parliament (September 2008) a party to whom payment is due is given additional rights with regard to suspension of works for non-payment:

1   that party may suspend only part of his works – currently he must suspend all of his works to exercise these rights;
2   that party is entitled to receive an extension of time for reasonable remobilisation requirements; and
3   that party is entitled to be paid his reasonable costs and expenses reasonably incurred as a result of the exercise of the right of suspension.

Conditional payment provisions

The 'pay when paid' clause was perhaps the one common feature of construction subcontracts that most offended the party who was hoping to be paid. Main contractors' terms of subcontract would be branded as aggressive if they contained such a clause and might be assumed benign if they did not.

There was surprisingly little case law dealing with them, perhaps because main contractors were reluctant to allow their clauses to be tested in court in case they were declared ineffective. There were many different versions, some designed to have a pay when paid effect without being obvious, and some drafted with added sophistication in the hope that they would prove effective. The object of course was to pass the risk of non-payment by an impecunious employer down to the subcontractor, or at least to share that risk with the subcontractor. A secondary object was to protect the main contractor's cash flow. Even if the employer was able to pay, the main contractor did not wish to pay out the value of the work to the subcontractors until he had been paid.

The subcontractor felt that this was fundamentally unfair. He had no direct contractual relationship with the employer, except perhaps through a collateral warranty dealing with quality of workmanship or design. He had no means of ensuring that payment would be made by the employer or of pressing him for payment within the agreed credit period. Although it had become politically incorrect to advance the opposite argument, main contractors also had a point. The process of construction on a large site was to some degree a partnership between all the contractors involved. The main contractor was a conduit through whom the benefits of a project would be passed down to the subcontractors, but relatively little of the profit would remain in his hands. The most profitable trade on the site might be one of the specialists, such as mechanical and electrical engineering. There was some justice in asking the specialist contractors to accept a portion of risk.

The draftsmen of the Act have taken a middle route in dealing with the pay when paid clause. Section 113(1) provides:

> '(1)   A provision making payment under a construction contract conditional on the payer receiving payment from a third person is ineffective, unless that third person, or any other person payment by whom is under the contract (directly or indirectly) a condition of payment by that person, is insolvent.'

In simple cases the effect of this section is quite clear. A traditional 'pay when paid' or 'pay if paid' clause in a subcontract is ineffective. The main contractor will not be able to delay or avoid payment to his subcontractor on the strength of such a clause, simply because the employer has not been paid. It is as if the clause was not there at all, and the normal payment provisions of the subcontract will apply.

If, however, the employer has not paid because he is insolvent, as defined by the Act, a traditional 'pay when paid' clause will be effective. The main contractor will be able to avoid paying the subcontractor. In this case the main contractor's position is stronger than before the Act, because there is no longer any doubt about the efficacy of the clause.

The position becomes rather less clear when there are other parties involved. The popular understanding of the section is that if there is an insolvency further up the chain of payment other than described above, that insolvency will be sufficient to make the conditional payment provisions in all the subsequent contracts effective. If the employer fails to pay because he is insolvent, the 'pay when paid' clause in the contract between the main contractor and the subcontractor will apply, and so will a 'pay when paid' clause in a sub-subcontract.

This is not, however, quite what the section says. Looking at the situation described in the preceding paragraph from the point of view of the sub-subcontractor, he wishes to know whether the 'pay when paid' clause in his contract with the first subcontractor is effective. The 'third person' who must pay the first subcontractor if the sub-subcontractor is to be paid is the main contractor. The main contractor is not insolvent. The insolvent party is the employer. Is the employer a 'person payment by whom is under the contract [i.e. the sub-subcontract] (directly or indirectly) a condition of payment by' the main contractor? It is unlikely that there will be a condition in the sub-subcontract dealing with payment by the main contractor to the first subcontractor. It may be argued that by inserting the words 'directly or indirectly' it is suggested that we are to consider the chain of payment in a simplistic way, but in the absence of any court decisions on this matter there must be considerable doubt.

A variant of the 'pay when paid' clause in common use before the Act was the 'pay when certified' clause. In an attempt to secure the cash-flow advantages of a 'pay when paid' clause without the opprobrium that surrounded such clauses, main contractors would include a provision linking payment under the subcontract to certification under the main contract. If the main contract payment term was 14 days after the date of a certificate, the subcontract would provide for payment, for example, 21 days after the relevant main contract certificate. If the certificate was too late, or was not given at all, the subcontractor would have to wait for payment.

There was some debate in the early days of the Act's passage through Parliament about whether s. 113 should be expanded to make such a clause ineffective as well, but those who wished to do so were unsuccessful. It is argued by those who wish to champion the subcontractors' cause that 'pay when certified' clauses are nevertheless ineffective, on the basis that the words 'receiving payment' in s. 113 do not just mean 'receiving cash'. They argue that a certificate is a chose in action or a debt, unless it is opened up, reviewed or revised in arbitration or litigation, as suggested in *Lubenham Fidelities and Investment Co Ltd v South Pembrokeshire DC and Wigley Fox Partnership* [1986] 33 BLR 39 and *Costain Building & Civil Engineering Ltd v Scottish Rugby Union plc* (1993) SC 650. 'Pay when certified' they argue therefore effectively becomes 'pay when paid' and is caught by the Act. Most commentators, however, consider that this is stretching the interpretation of the section too far.

It is also argued that whilst a 'pay when certified' clause may not be rendered ineffective by s. 113, it does not provide an 'adequate mechanism for determining what payments become due under the contract and when', and that accordingly s. 110 will intervene to impose the Scheme, rendering the 'pay when certified' clause redundant. The lack of an objective test for determining what is adequate makes it impossible to argue the case with certainty, but a provision that money will become due a specific number of days before or after an event such as the issue of a certificate under the main contract would seem capable of providing a mechanism that is workable and clear. To that extent it would seem to be adequate, if undesirable from the point of view of the subcontractor.

Although the draft Bill currently before Parliament (September 2008) does not propose any amendments to s. 113 it does propose an amendment to s. 110 to the effect that payment terms that are conditional on the performance of obligations under another contract are not an adequate mechanism for determining what payments become due and when. If this provision were to be enacted it would render pay when certified clauses ineffective.

Section 113(2) to (5) defines insolvency:

'(2) For the purposes of this section a company becomes insolvent –
   (a) on the making of an administration order against it under Part II of the Insolvency Act 1986,
   (b) on the appointment of an administrative receiver or a receiver or manager of its property under Chapter I of Part III of that Act, or the appointment of a receiver under Chapter II of that Part,
   (c) on the passing of a resolution for voluntary winding-up without a declaration of solvency under section 89 of that Act, or
   (d) on the making of a winding-up order under Part IV or V of that Act.
(3) For the purposes of this section a partnership becomes insolvent –
   (a) on the making of a winding-up order against it under any provision of the Insolvency Act 1986 as applied by an order under section 420 of that Act, or
   (b) when sequestration is awarded on the estate of the partnership under section 12 of the Bankruptcy (Scotland) Act 1985 or the partnership grants a trust deed for its creditors.
(4) For the purposes of this section an individual becomes insolvent –
   (a) on the making of a bankruptcy order against him under Part IX of the Insolvency Act 1986, or
   (b) on the sequestration of his estate under the Bankruptcy (Scotland) Act 1985 or when he grants a trust deed for his creditors.
(5) A company, partnership or individual shall also be treated as insolvent on the occurrence of any event corresponding to those specified in subsection (2), (3) or (4) under the law of Northern Ireland or of a country outside the United Kingdom.'

It should be noted that this list is not the same as the list of circumstances included as 'insolvency' in many contracts.

The Scheme also contains a provision relating to conditional payments, providing what is to happen if s. 113 of the Act has operated and effectively destroyed the payment mechanism in the contract that relied on the conditional payment clause.

Paragraph 11 of Part II of the Scheme provides:

> '11 Where a provision making payment under a construction contract conditional on the payer receiving payment from a third person is ineffective as mentioned in section 113 of the Act, and the parties have not agreed other terms for payment, the relevant provisions of –
>
> (a)   paragraphs 2, 4, 5, 7, 8, 9 and 10 shall apply in the case of a relevant construction contract, and
> (b)   paragraphs 6, 7, 8, 9 and 10 shall apply in the case of any other construction contract.'

A 'relevant construction contract' is a contract other than one that specifies that the work is to be of less than 45 days duration or in respect of which the parties agree that the work is estimated to be of less than 45 days duration. The effect of this paragraph is simply to ensure that the Scheme will apply not only where no agreement has been reached providing an adequate mechanism for dealing with payments, but also where the mechanism has been declared ineffective.

Frequently asked questions

Q. Does a contractor have a right to suspend works for non-payment even where the HGCRA 1996 does not apply?

A. Generally, a contractor does not have a right to suspend for non-payment where the HGCRA 1996 does not apply. However, there are some exceptions. If the client's failure to pay evinces an intention on the part of the client no longer to be bound by the terms of the contract then that will amount to a repudiatory breach which the contractor can accept thereby bringing the contract to an end. Late payment by the client will generally not amount to a repudiatory breach so long as the client intends to pay. However, if the client no longer intends to pay for works done then that will be a repudiatory breach. Also, if the contractor is a small company, late payment by the client may prevent the contractor from paying his own suppliers and subcontractors and thereby unable to secure labour or materials to continue with the works. Such action may amount to an act of prevention by the client. See Lord Asquith in *Cory Ltd v City of London Corp* [1951] 2 KB 476 at 484.

Q. Are pay when paid clauses unlawful now?

A. Section 113 of HGCRA 1996 effectively states that pay when paid clauses shall be of no effect unless that third party is insolvent. Therefore a pay when paid clause is not unlawful it is just ineffective. Further, like the other payment provisions s. 113 only applies where HGCRA 1996 applies. Therefore there are no restrictions on pay when paid clauses, for example in contracts with residential occupiers, in contracts for the installation of plant in many process plant applications or in contracts that are not wholly recorded in writing.

9

Contractor's remedies

Introduction

In this chapter, attention is focused upon the *remedies* available to a party who considers that it has been underpaid, or who has not been paid at all. The starting point, as in other issues, will be the express terms of the contract (if there is a contract at all).

There are, however, a number of important principles which ought to inform a party who has not been paid:

- There is an important distribution between claims made under the terms of a contract, and claims for damages for breach of contract. Only in the cases where the clearest words are used in the contract will the express terms deprive a party from claiming damages for breach of contract as an alternative to claims under the express terms.
- The obligation to pay, whether on time or at all, will generally be regarded as a *warranty* and not a *condition*. This is an important legal distinction with real practical significance. Since a failure to pay will only amount to a breach of *warranty*, the defaulting party will not be in repudiatory breach of contract by paying late. This is important as it is only for repudiatory breaches of contract (i.e. conduct evincing an intention on the part of the defaulting party not to be bound by the contract) that the innocent party can bring an end to the contract and, in practical terms, pull off the job. In other words, there is no right at common law to suspend work for non-payment.
- An express right to suspend for non-payment will – apart from where s. 112 of HGCRA 1996 is involved or replicated in a contract, see below – be quite rare. However, where provisions of this kind *do* exist, then they must be operated with great care. Just as with termination provisions, where

a party fails to follow the required procedures exactly, then he will risk placing himself in repudiatory breach of contract.

Express provisions for disruption and prolongation

Delay and disruption are very common problems in the construction industry. When a project is prolonged beyond the anticipated completion date, the contractor may incur extra costs and potentially liquidated damages for late completion. The construction industry has responded to these problems with express terms in the standard form contracts, and the law has responded by clarifying the default position.

The NEC Contract

The NEC Contract manages disruption and employer's prevention with the concept of 'compensation events'. All options contain the following relevant compensation events:

- clause 60.1(1): the project manager changes the works information;
- clause 60.1(2): the employer prevents access to the site;
- clause 60.1(3): the employer does not provide something on time;
- clause 60.1(4): the project manager gives an instruction to stop or not to start any work or to change a key date;
- clause. 60.1(5): the employer does not follow the programme or works information;
- clause 60.1(6): the project manager/supervisor fails to respond to the contractor's communication within the specified time;
- clause 60.1(8): the project manager or the supervisor changes a decision which he has previously communicated to the contractor;
- clause 60.1(11): a test/inspection by the supervisor causes unnecessary delay;
- clause 60.1(12): the contractor encounters unforeseen physical conditions;
- clause 60.1(13): the contractor encounters unforeseen weather conditions;
- clause 60.1(16): the employer does not provide the required materials, facilities, samples or inspections;
- clause 60.1(18): any other breach by the employer;

- clause 60.1(19): any other unforeseen delay-causing event which neither party could prevent.

The compensation event process is governed by clauses 61 to 63. Normally the contractor will submit quotations for amendments to the price or time for completion. These amendments may be revised, negotiated, accepted or rejected by the project manager. The diagram below illustrates the NEC compensation event process.

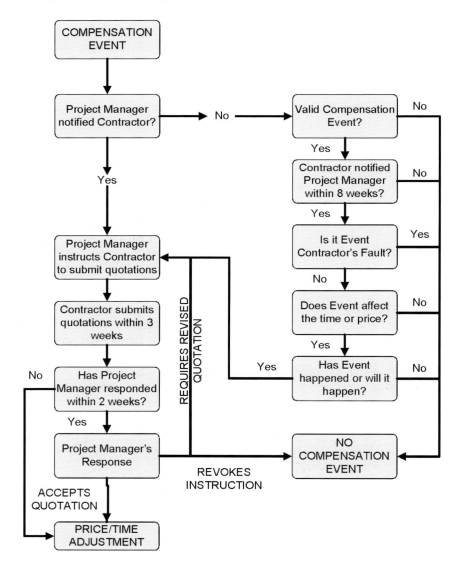

The FIDIC Contract

Clause 8.4 of FIDIC entitles the contractor to an extension of the time for completion if completion is or will be delayed by any of the following causes:

1   a variation (unless agreed) or other substantial change in the quantity of an item of work included in the contract;
2   a cause of delay giving an entitlement to extension of time under a subclause of FIDIC;
3   exceptionally adverse climatic conditions;
4   unforeseeable shortages in the availability of personnel or goods caused by epidemic or governmental actions; or
5   any delay, impediment or prevention caused by or attributable to the employer, the employer's personnel, or the employer's other contractors on the site.

The common law

In the absence of express provision for disruption, prolongation and non-payment, the common law provides basic remedies.

Merton LBC v Stanley Hugh Leach Ltd [1986] 32 BLR 51 is authority for an implied term that the employer must not do anything to hinder or prevent the contractor from performing his obligations under the contract.

Where an employer has disrupted the course of the works, he will not be able to claim liquidated damages for any delay caused by his own disruption (provided the contractor has complied with any relevant formal notice requirements) under the 'prevention principle' (see Chapter 5 on notices and the prevention principle).

If the employer's action requires the contractor to remain on site longer than anticipated, he would normally obtain prolongation costs as a variation under the contract. Where there is no such express mechanism, he may be entitled to a *quantum meruit* payment for extra work done (see Chapter 2 on *quantum meruit*) or damages for breach of contract to cover losses and/or additional costs.

Global claims

Where a contractor has multiple claims for disruption and/or prolongation, but perhaps due to the complexity of the project is unable to specify causation, loss and damage for each individual breach, he may issue a 'global claim'. Global claims (also called 'total cost claims' or 'rolled-up claims') are claims based on multiple events which give rise to a single entitlement. These events might include variations, compensation events or breaches of contracts.

In the Australian case of *John Holland Construction v Kvaerner RJ Brown* [1996] 82 BLR 83, Byrne J provided the following definition of a global claim:

> 'The claim as pleaded . . . is a global claim, that is, the claimant does not seek to attribute any specific loss to a specific breach of contract, but is content to allege a composite loss as a result of all the breaches alleged, or presumably as a result of such breaches as are ultimately proved.'

The law has been traditionally hostile to global claims, not least because they offend against the basic tenets of proper pleading. They fail to address causation and *quantum*, they fail to adequately particularise each claim, and they can potentially be used to disguise other reasons for delay (e.g. underpriced tender or contractor's inefficiency). This 'traditional' position is neatly summarised by the dicta of Lord Oliver in *Wharf Properties v Eric Cumine Associates (No 2)* [1991] 52 BLR 8:

> ' . . . the pleading is hopelessly embarrassing as it stands . . . in cases where the full extent of extra costs incurred through delay depend upon a complex interaction between the consequences of various events, so that it may be difficult to make an accurate apportionment of the total extra costs, it may be proper for an arbitrator to make individual financial awards in respect of claims which can conveniently be dealt with in isolation and a supplementary award in respect of the financial consequences of the remainder as a composite whole. This has, however, no bearing upon the obligation of a plaintiff to plead his case with such particularity as is sufficient to alert the opposite party to the case which is going to be made against him at the trial.'

From this basic position, the law has 'carved out' several exceptions, such that the courts are now more willing to permit global claims in certain circumstances. The following cases illustrate the erosion of the 'traditional' view.

J. Crosby & Sons Ltd v Portland Urban District Council [1967] 5 BLR 121

Crosby contracted with Portland UDC to lay a 15 inch trunk water main. The works were delayed by 46 weeks for various reasons, some of which should have entitled Crosby to additional time/money and some of which did not. Donaldson J held that the arbitrator was permitted to make a global award in respect of all of the claims. He said:

> 'I can see no reason why (the arbitrator) should not recognise the realities of the situation and make individual awards in respect of those parts of individual items of the claim which can be dealt with in isolation and a supplementary award in respect of the remainder of these claims as a composite whole.'

Merton LBC v Stanley Hugh Leach Ltd [1985] 32 BLR 51

Merton engaged SHL to construct 287 dwellings. The works were delayed, and SHL contended that this was due to want of diligence, care and a general lack of co-operation on the part of Merton's architect. In dealing with what was, in effect, a global claim, Vinelott J said:

> 'If application is made ... for reimbursement of direct loss and expense attributable to more than one head of claim and at the time when the loss or expense comes to be ascertained, it is impractical to disentangle or disintegrate the part directly attributable to each head of claim then, provided of course that the contractor has not unreasonably delayed in making the claim and so has himself created the difficulty, the architect must ascertain the global loss attributable to the two causes ...'

Mid Glamorgan County Council v J Devonald Williams & Partner [1992] 29 Con LR 129

Mid Glamorgan County Council engaged a firm of architects to supervise and run a project at Rhondda College of Further

Education. The architects caused various delays, and the Council issued a global claim. Despite repeated requests for further and better particulars, the Council were unable to particularise every delay within their claim. Mr Recorder Tackaberry QC noted that, whilst the burden usually fell to the claimant to make clear his claim, in these circumstances the claimant had done all it reasonably could to particularise the delays and, notwithstanding that many claims remained 'rolled up', held that the action could proceed.

Bernhards Rugby Landscapes Ltd v Stockley Park Consortium Ltd [1997] 82 BLR 39

A party must set out its case with 'sufficient particularity', and state the nexus of causation/interaction of events with adequate clarity. Whilst a claimant may of course plead its claim on liability or *quantum* as it sees fit, the defendant is entitled to know what case it has to meet. 'Sufficient particularity' is a matter of fact and degree in each case; a balance must be struck between excessive particularity and basic information.

Laing Management Ltd v John Doyle Construction Ltd [2004] BLR 295

John Doyle were engaged by Laing Management to undertake work on the new headquarters for the Scottish Widow's Fund and Life Assurance Society in Edinburgh. John Doyle sought an extension of time of 22 weeks, a claim for loss and expense, and a claim upon the final account arising from multiple breaches by Laing Management. The Extra Division of the Scottish Inner House Court of Session made the following findings:

- For a loss and expense claim in normal circumstances, the contractor must show breach, loss and causation for each individual event.
- If the contractor can demonstrate that all of the events are the responsibility of the employer, it is not necessary for him to demonstrate causal links between individual events and particular heads of loss.
- Where not all events can be traced back to the employer, the court may nevertheless allow a global claim where the contractor can show that the employer's acts were the 'dominant cause' of his loss.
- A global claim must not be advanced in lieu of proper pleading. The contractor's claim should still satisfy the fundamental requirements of any pleadings, namely that

they should give fair notice to the other party of the facts that are relied on, together with the general structure of the legal consequences that are said to follow from those facts.

London Underground Ltd v Citylink Telecommunications Ltd [2007] EWHC 1749

London Underground engaged Citylink to install communications systems across its network. Citylink argued that a number of breaches by London Underground had caused significant delays, and referred the matter to arbitration. The arbitrator followed the approach in *Laing Management*. Ramsey J endorsed this approach, and the jurisprudence of Laing Management. He held that, although normally the claimant must show that the defendant is liable for all events comprising the global claim, there may be circumstances in which the court may carry out an 'apportionment exercise', granting costs to the extent that causation could be established.

The courts in recent years have taken a more pragmatic approach towards global claims, relaxing the 'traditional' stance taken in *Wharf Properties*. Notwithstanding this, however, a potential claimant should remember that a global claim is still only permissible when it is impossible to attribute a specific loss to a specific event, and that any claim will still be regarded with some degree of caution.

Frequently asked questions

Q. Can a contractor still make a global claim for delay and disruption costs?

A. A contractor can make a global claim but it is unlikely to be successful before a tribunal unless the contractor has made every effort to separate out those costs that can be separately attributable to separate events and it is reasonably apparent that the remaining costs were caused by events for which the client is liable. Of course many global claims are advanced at an early stage of negotiations to indicate the eventual potential size of the claim once all of the work has been done assuming that settlement negotiations are not successful. Such claims are a perfectly proper part of negotiations even though a claim relying solely on that basis is unlikely to succeed in formal dispute resolution proceedings.

Q. Can a contractor claim damages for breach of contract even where there is a provision dealing with recovery of costs for delay and disruption?

A. Generally a contractor can claim damages for breach of contract as an alternative to relying on the contractual mechanism for recovering additional costs. See *Merton LBC v Stanley Hugh Leach Ltd* [1986] 32 BLR 51 at 105-109. This is often a useful strategy where the contractual process has become frustrated, for example if a condition to payment under the contract has not been satisfied. However, if the contract contains an exclusive remedies clause (as many bespoke or amended contracts do) then the contractor effectively waives his rights to claim damages as an alternative claim.

Appendix 1 – HGCRA 1996, ss 104-107 and 109-113

Part II Construction contracts

Introductory provisions

104 Construction contracts

(1) In this Part a "construction contract" means an agreement with a person for any of the following—
- (a) the carrying out of construction operations;
- (b) arranging for the carrying out of construction operations by others, whether under sub-contract to him or otherwise;
- (c) providing his own labour, or the labour of others, for the carrying out of construction operations.

(2) References in this Part to a construction contract include an agreement—
- (a) to do architectural, design, or surveying work, or
- (b) to provide advice on building, engineering, interior or exterior decoration or on the laying-out of landscape,

in relation to construction operations.

(3) References in this Part to a construction contract do not include a contract of employment (within the meaning of the [1996 c. 18.] Employment Rights Act 1996).

(4) The Secretary of State may by order add to, amend or repeal any of the provisions of subsection (1), (2) or (3) as to the agreements which are construction contracts for the purposes of this Part or are to be taken or not to be taken as included in references to such contracts.

No such order shall be made unless a draft of it has been laid before and approved by a resolution of each of House of Parliament.

(5) Where an agreement relates to construction operations and other matters, this Part applies to it only so far as it relates to construction operations.

An agreement relates to construction operations so far as it makes provision of any kind within subsection (1) or (2).

(6) This Part applies only to construction contracts which—
- (a) are entered into after the commencement of this Part, and

171

  (b) relate to the carrying out of construction operations in England, Wales or Scotland.

(7) This Part applies whether or not the law of England and Wales or Scotland is otherwise the applicable law in relation to the contract.

105 Meaning of "construction operations"

(1) In this Part "construction operations" means, subject as follows, operations of any of the following descriptions—

  (a) construction, alteration, repair, maintenance, extension, demolition or dismantling of buildings, or structures forming, or to form, part of the land (whether permanent or not);

  (b) construction, alteration, repair, maintenance, extension, demolition or dismantling of any works forming, or to form, part of the land, including (without prejudice to the foregoing) walls, roadworks, power-lines, telecommunication apparatus, aircraft runways, docks and harbours, railways, inland waterways, pipe-lines, reservoirs, water-mains, wells, sewers, industrial plant and installations for purposes of land drainage, coast protection or defence;

  (c) installation in any building or structure of fittings forming part of the land, including (without prejudice to the foregoing) systems of heating, lighting, air-conditioning, ventilation, power supply, drainage, sanitation, water supply or fire protection, or security or communications systems;

  (d) external or internal cleaning of buildings and structures, so far as carried out in the course of their construction, alteration, repair, extension or restoration;

  (e) operations which form an integral part of, or are preparatory to, or are for rendering complete, such operations as are previously described in this subsection, including site clearance, earth-moving, excavation, tunnelling and boring, laying of foundations, erection, maintenance or dismantling of scaffolding, site restoration, landscaping and the provision of roadways and other access works;

  (f) painting or decorating the internal or external surfaces of any building or structure.

(2) The following operations are not construction operations within the meaning of this Part—

  (a) drilling for, or extraction of, oil or natural gas;

(b) extraction (whether by underground or surface working) of minerals; tunnelling or boring, or construction of underground works, for this purpose;

(c) assembly, installation or demolition of plant or machinery, or erection or demolition of steelwork for the purposes of supporting or providing access to plant or machinery, on a site where the primary activity is—

    (i) nuclear processing, power generation, or water or effluent treatment, or

    (ii) the production, transmission, processing or bulk storage (other than warehousing) of chemicals, pharmaceuticals, oil, gas, steel or food and drink;

(d) manufacture or delivery to site of—

    (i) building or engineering components or equipment,

    (ii) materials, plant or machinery, or

    (iii) components for systems of heating, lighting, air-conditioning, ventilation, power supply, drainage, sanitation, water supply or fire protection, or for security or communications systems,

except under a contract which also provides for their installation;

(e) the making, installation and repair of artistic works, being sculptures, murals and other works which are wholly artistic in nature.

(3) The Secretary of State may by order add to, amend or repeal any of the provisions of subsection (1) or (2) as to the operations and work to be treated as construction operations for the purposes of this Part.

(4) No such order shall be made unless a draft of it has been laid before and approved by a resolution of each House of Parliament.

106 Provisions not applicable to contract with residential occupier

(1) This Part does not apply—

(a) to a construction contract with a residential occupier (see below), or

(b) to any other description of construction contract excluded from the operation of this Part by order of the Secretary of State.

(2) A construction contract with a residential occupier means a construction contract which principally relates to operations on a dwelling which one of the parties to the contract occupies, or intends to occupy, as his residence.

In this subsection "dwelling" means a dwelling-house or a flat; and for this purpose—

"dwelling-house" does not include a building containing a flat; and

"flat" means separate and self-contained premises constructed or adapted for use for residential purposes and forming part of a building from some other part of which the premises are divided horizontally.

(3) The Secretary of State may by order amend subsection (2).

(4) No order under this section shall be made unless a draft of it has been laid before and approved by a resolution of each House of Parliament.

107 Provisions applicable only to agreements in writing

(1) The provisions of this Part apply only where the construction contract is in writing, and any other agreement between the parties as to any matter is effective for the purposes of this Part only if in writing.

The expressions "agreement", "agree" and "agreed" shall be construed accordingly.

(2) There is an agreement in writing—
    (a)   if the agreement is made in writing (whether or not it is signed by the parties),
    (b)   if the agreement is made by exchange of communications in writing, or
    (c)   if the agreement is evidenced in writing.

(3) Where parties agree otherwise than in writing by reference to terms which are in writing, they make an agreement in writing.

(4) An agreement is evidenced in writing if an agreement made otherwise than in writing is recorded by one of the parties, or by a third party, with the authority of the parties to the agreement.

(5) An exchange of written submissions in adjudication proceedings, or in arbitral or legal proceedings in which the existence of an agreement otherwise than in writing is alleged by one party against another party and not denied by the other party in his response constitutes as between those parties an agreement in writing to the effect alleged.

(6) References in this Part to anything being written or in writing include its being recorded by any means.

Payment

109 Entitlement to stage payments

(1) A party to a construction contract is entitled to payment by instalments, stage payments or other periodic payments for any work under the contract unless—

    (a)   it is specified in the contract that the duration of the work is to be less than 45 days, or

    (b)   it is agreed between the parties that the duration of the work is estimated to be less than 45 days.

(2) The parties are free to agree the amounts of the payments and the intervals at which, or circumstances in which, they become due.

(3) In the absence of such agreement, the relevant provisions of the Scheme for Construction Contracts apply.

(4) References in the following sections to a payment under the contract include a payment by virtue of this section.

110 Dates for payment

(1) Every construction contract shall—

    (a)   provide an adequate mechanism for determining what payments become due under the contract, and when, and

    (b)   provide for a final date for payment in relation to any sum which becomes due.

The parties are free to agree how long the period is to be between the date on which a sum becomes due and the final date for payment.

(2) Every construction contract shall provide for the giving of notice by a party not later than five days after the date on which a payment becomes due from him under the contract, or would have become due if—

    (a)   the other party had carried out his obligations under the contract, and

    (b)   no set-off or abatement was permitted by reference to any sum claimed to be due under one or more other contracts,

specifying the amount (if any) of the payment made or proposed to be made, and the basis on which that amount was calculated.

(3) If or to the extent that a contract does not contain such provision as is mentioned in subsection (1) or (2), the relevant provisions of the Scheme for Construction Contracts apply.

111 Notice of intention to withhold payment

(1) A party to a construction contract may not withhold payment after the final date for payment of a sum due under the contract unless he has given an effective notice of intention to withhold payment.

The notice mentioned in section 110(2) may suffice as a notice of intention to withhold payment if it complies with the requirements of this section.

(2) To be effective such a notice must specify—
    (a)   the amount proposed to be withheld and the ground for withholding payment, or
    (b)   if there is more than one ground, each ground and the amount attributable to it,

and must be given not later than the prescribed period before the final date for payment.

(3) The parties are free to agree what that prescribed period is to be.

In the absence of such agreement, the period shall be that provided by the Scheme for Construction Contracts.

(4) Where an effective notice of intention to withhold payment is given, but on the matter being referred to adjudication it is decided that the whole or part of the amount should be paid, the decision shall be construed as requiring payment not later than—
    (a)   seven days from the date of the decision, or
    (b)   the date which apart from the notice would have been the final date for payment,

whichever is the later.

112 Right to suspend performance for non-payment

(1) Where a sum due under a construction contract is not paid in full by the final date for payment and no effective notice to withhold payment has been given, the person to whom the sum is due has the right (without prejudice to any other right or remedy) to suspend performance of his obligations under the contract to the party by whom payment ought to have been made ("the party in default").

(2) The right may not be exercised without first giving to the party in default at least seven days' notice of intention to suspend performance, stating the ground or grounds on which it is intended to suspend performance.

(3) The right to suspend performance ceases when the party in default makes payment in full of the amount due.

(4) Any period during which performance is suspended in pursuance of the right conferred by this section shall be disregarded in computing for the purposes of any

contractual time limit the time taken, by the party exercising the right or by a third party, to complete any work directly or indirectly affected by the exercise of the right.

Where the contractual time limit is set by reference to a date rather than a period, the date shall be adjusted accordingly.

113 Prohibition of conditional payment provisions

(1) A provision making payment under a construction contract conditional on the payer receiving payment from a third person is ineffective, unless that third person, or any other person payment by whom is under the contract (directly or indirectly) a condition of payment by that third person, is insolvent.

(2) For the purposes of this section a company becomes insolvent—

    (a)   on the making of an administration order against it under Part II of the [1986 c. 45.] Insolvency Act 1986,

    (b)   on the appointment of an administrative receiver or a receiver or manager of its property under Chapter I of Part III of that Act, or the appointment of a receiver under Chapter II of that Part,

    (c)   on the passing of a resolution for voluntary winding-up without a declaration of solvency under section 89 of that Act, or

    (d)   on the making of a winding-up order under Part IV or V of that Act.

(3) For the purposes of this section a partnership becomes insolvent—

    (a)   on the making of a winding-up order against it under any provision of the Insolvency Act 1986 as applied by an order under section 420 of that Act, or

    (b)   when sequestration is awarded on the estate of the partnership under section 12 of the [1985 c. 66.] Bankruptcy (Scotland) Act 1985 or the partnership grants a trust deed for its creditors.

(4) For the purposes of this section an individual becomes insolvent—

    (a)   on the making of a bankruptcy order against him under Part IX of the [1986 c. 45.] Insolvency Act 1986, or

      (b)   on the sequestration of his estate under the Bankruptcy (Scotland) Act 1985 or when he grants a trust deed for his creditors.

(5) A company, partnership or individual shall also be treated as insolvent on the occurrence of any event corresponding to those specified in subsection (2), (3) or (4) under the law of Northern Ireland or of a country outside the United Kingdom.

(6) Where a provision is rendered ineffective by subsection (1), the parties are free to agree other terms for payment.

In the absence of such agreement, the relevant provisions of the Scheme for Construction Contracts apply.

Appendix 2 – Scheme for Construction Contracts (England and Wales) Regulations 1998

(SI 1998/649)

PART II – PAYMENT

Entitlement to and amount of stage payments

1. Where the parties to a relevant construction contract fail to agree—

(a)   the amount of any instalment or stage or periodic payment for any work under the contract, or

(b)   the intervals at which, or circumstances in which, such payments become due under that contract, or

(c)   both of the matters mentioned in sub-paragraphs (a) and (b) above,

the relevant provisions of paragraphs 2 to 4 below shall apply.

2. -

(1) The amount of any payment by way of instalments or stage or periodic payments in respect of a relevant period shall be the difference between the amount determined in accordance with sub-paragraph (2) and the amount determined in accordance with sub-paragraph (3).

(2) The aggregate of the following amounts—

(a)   an amount equal to the value of any work performed in accordance with the relevant construction contract during the period from the commencement of the contract to the end of the relevant period (excluding any amount calculated in accordance with sub-paragraph (b)),

(b)   where the contract provides for payment for materials, an amount equal to the value of any materials manufactured on site or brought onto site for the purposes of the works during the period from the commencement of the contract to the end of the relevant period, and

      (c)   any other amount or sum which the contract specifies shall be payable during or in respect of the period from the commencement of the contract to the end of the relevant period.

(3) The aggregate of any sums which have been paid or are due for payment by way of instalments, stage or periodic payments during the period from the commencement of the contract to the end of the relevant period.

(4) An amount calculated in accordance with this paragraph shall not exceed the difference between—

      (a)   the contract price, and

      (b)   the aggregate of the instalments or stage or periodic payments which have become due.

Dates for payment

3. Where the parties to a construction contract fail to provide an adequate mechanism for determining either what payments become due under the contract, or when they become due for payment, or both, the relevant provisions of paragraphs 4 to 7 shall apply.

4. Any payment of a kind mentioned in paragraph 2 above shall become due on whichever of the following dates occurs later—

(a)   the expiry of 7 days following the relevant period mentioned in paragraph 2(1) above, or

(b)   the making of a claim by the payee.

5. The final payment payable under a relevant construction contract, namely the payment of an amount equal to the difference (if any) between—

(a)   the contract price, and

(b)   the aggregate of any instalment or stage or periodic payments which have become due under the contract,

shall become due on the expiry of—

(a)   30 days following completion of the work, or

(b)   the making of a claim by the payee,

whichever is the later.

6. Payment of the contract price under a construction contract (not being a relevant construction contract) shall become due on—

(a)   the expiry of 30 days following the completion of the work, or

(b)   the making of a claim by the payee,

whichever is the later.

7. Any other payment under a construction contract shall become due—
(a)   on the expiry of 7 days following the completion of the work to which the payment relates, or
(b)   the making of a claim by the payee,

whichever is the later.

Final date for payment

8. -
(1) Where the parties to a construction contract fail to provide a final date for payment in relation to any sum which becomes due under a construction contract, the provisions of this paragraph shall apply.
(2) The final date for the making of any payment of a kind mentioned in paragraphs 2, 5, 6 or 7, shall be 17 days from the date that payment becomes due.

Notice specifying amount of payment

9. A party to a construction contract shall, not later than 5 days after the date on which any payment—
(a)   becomes due from him, or
(b)   would have become due, if—
    (i)   the other party had carried out his obligations under the contract, and
    (ii)   no set-off or abatement was permitted by reference to any sum claimed to be due under one or more other contracts,

give notice to the other party to the contract specifying the amount (if any) of the payment he has made or proposes to make, specifying to what the payment relates and the basis on which that amount is calculated.

Notice of intention to withhold payment

10. Any notice of intention to withhold payment mentioned in section 111 of the Act shall be given not later than the prescribed period, which is to say not later than 7 days before the final date for payment determined either in accordance with the construction contract, or where no such provision is made in the contract, in accordance with paragraph 8 above.

Prohibition of conditional payment provisions

11. Where a provision making payment under a construction contract conditional on the payer receiving payment from a third person is ineffective as mentioned in section 113 of the Act, and the parties have not agreed other terms for payment, the relevant provisions of—
(a)   paragraphs 2, 4, 5, 7, 8, 9 and 10 shall apply in the case of a relevant construction contract, and
(b)   paragraphs 6, 7, 8, 9 and 10 shall apply in the case of any other construction contract.

Interpretation

12. In this Part of the Scheme for Construction Contracts—

"claim by the payee" means a written notice given by the party carrying out work under a construction contract to the other party specifying the amount of any payment or payments which he considers to be due and the basis on which it is, or they are, calculated;

"contract price" means the entire sum payable under the construction contract in respect of the work;

"relevant construction contract" means any construction contract other than one—
(a)   which specifies that the duration of the work is to be less than 45 days, or
(b)   in respect of which the parties agree that the duration of the work is estimated to be less than 45 days;

"relevant period" means a period which is specified in, or is calculated by reference to the construction contract or where no such period is so specified or is so calculable, a period of 28 days;

"value of work" means an amount determined in accordance with the construction contract under which the work is performed or where the contract contains no such provision, the cost of any work performed in accordance with that contract together with an amount equal to any overhead or profit included in the contract price;

"work" means any of the work or services mentioned in section 104 of the Act.

Appendix 3 – Scheme for Construction Contracts (Scotland) Regulations 1998

(SI 1998/687)

PART II PAYMENT

Entitlement to and amount of stage payments

1. Where the parties to a relevant construction contract fail to agree—

(a)   the amount of any instalment or stage or periodic payment for any work under the contract;

(b)   the intervals at which, or circumstances in which, such payments become due under that contract; or

(c)   both of the matters mentioned in sub-paragraphs (a) and (b),

the relevant provisions of paragraphs 2 to 4 shall apply.

2. -

(1) The amount of any payment by way of instalments or stage or periodic payments in respect of a relevant period shall be the difference between the amount determined in accordance with sub-paragraph (2) and the amount determined in accordance with sub-paragraph (3).

(2) The aggregate of the following amounts:—

(a)   an amount equal to the value of any work performed in accordance with the relevant construction contract during the period from the commencement of the contract to the end of the relevant period (excluding any amount calculated in accordance with head (b));

(b)   where the contract provides for payment for materials, an amount equal to the value of any materials manufactured on site or brought onto site for the purposes of the works during the period from the commencement of the contract to the end of the relevant period; and

    (c)   any other amount or sum which the contract specifies shall be payable during or in respect of the period from the commencement of the contract to the end of the relevant period.

(3) The aggregate of any sums which have been paid or are due for payment by way of instalments, stage or periodic payments during the period from the commencement of the contract to the end of the relevant period.

(4) An amount calculated in accordance with this paragraph shall not exceed the difference between-

    (a)   the contract price; and

    (b)   the aggregate of the instalments or stage or periodic payments which have become due.

Dates for payment

3. Where the parties to a construction contract fail to provide an adequate mechanism for determining either what payments become due under the contract, or when they become due for payment, or both, the relevant provisions of paragraphs 4 to 7 shall apply.

4. Any payment of a kind mentioned in paragraph 2 above shall become due on whichever of the following dates occurs later:—

(a)   the expiry of 7 days following the relevant period mentioned in paragraph 2(1); or

(b)   the making of a claim by the payee.

5. The final payment payable under a relevant construction contract, namely the payment of an amount equal to the difference (if any) between—

(a)   the contract price; and

(b)   the aggregate of any instalment or stage or periodic payments which have become due under the contract,

shall become due on—

(i)   the expiry of 30 days following completion of the work; or

(ii)   the making of a claim by the payee,

whichever is the later.

6. Payment of the contract price under a construction contract (not being a relevant construction contract) shall become due on—

(a)   the expiry of 30 days following the completion of the work; or

(b)   the making of a claim by the payee,

whichever is the later.

7. Any other payment under a construction contract shall become due on—

(a)   the expiry of 7 days following the completion of the work to which the payment relates; or

(b)   the making of a claim by the payee,

whichever is the later.

Final date for payment

8. -

(1) Where the parties to a construction contract fail to provide a final date for payment in relation to any sum which becomes due under a construction contract, the provisions of this paragraph shall apply.

(2) The final date for the making of any payment of a kind mentioned in paragraph 2, 5, 6 or 7 shall be 17 days from the date that payment becomes due.

Notice specifying amount of payment

9. A party to a construction contract shall, not later than 5 days after the date on which any payment-

(a)   becomes due from him; or

(b)   would have become due, if-

   (i)   the other party had carried out his obligations under the contract; and

   (ii)   no set-off or abatement was permitted by reference to any sum claimed to be due under one or more other contracts,

give notice to the other party to the contract specifying the amount (if any) of the payment he has made or proposes to make, specifying to what the payment relates and the basis on which that amount is calculated.

Notice of intention to withhold payment

10. Any notice of intention to withhold payment mentioned in section 111 of the Act shall be given not later than the prescribed period, which is to say not later than 7 days before the final date for payment determined either in accordance with the construction contract or, where no such provision is made in the contract, in accordance with paragraph 8.

Prohibition of conditional payment provisions

11. Where a provision making payment under a construction contract conditional on the payer receiving payment from a third person is ineffective as mentioned in section 113 of the Act and the parties have not agreed other terms for payment, the relevant provisions of—

(a)   paragraphs 2, 4, 5, and 7 to 10 shall apply in the case of a relevant construction contract; and

(b)   paragraphs 6 to 10 shall apply in the case of any other construction contract.

Interpretation

12. In this Part—

"claim by the payee" means a written notice given by the party carrying out work under a construction contract to the other party specifying the amount of any payment or payments which he considers to be due, specifying to what the payment relates (or payments relate) and the basis on which it is, or they are, calculated;

"contract price" means the entire sum payable under the construction contract in respect of the work;

"relevant construction contract" means any construction contract other than one—

(a)   which specifies that the duration of the work is to be less than 45 days, or

(b)   in respect of which the parties agree that the duration of the work is estimated to be less than 45 days;

"relevant period" means a period which is specified in, or is calculated by reference to, the construction contract or, where no such period is so specified or is so calculable, a period of 28 days;

"value of work" means an amount determined in accordance with the construction contract under which the work is performed or, where the contract contains no such provision, the cost of any work performed in accordance with that contract together with an amount equal to any overhead or profit included in the contract price;

"work" means any of the work or services mentioned in section 104 of the Act.

Appendix 4 – Scheme for Construction Contracts in Northern Ireland Regulations (Northern Ireland) 1999

(SI 1999/32)

PART II PAYMENT

Entitlement to and amount of stage payments

1. Where the parties to a relevant construction contract fail to agree—
(a) the amount of any instalment or stage or periodic payment for any work under the contract;
(b) the intervals at which, or circumstances in which, such payments become due under that contract; or
(c) both of the matters mentioned in sub-paragraphs (a) and (b),

the relevant provisions of paragraphs 2 to 4 shall apply.

2. -
(1) The amount of any payment by way of instalments or stage or periodic payments in respect of a relevant period shall be the difference between the amount determined in accordance with sub-paragraph (2) and the amount determined in accordance with sub-paragraph (3).
(2) The aggregate of the following amounts—
(a) an amount equal to the value of any work performed in accordance with the relevant construction contract during the period from the commencement of the contract to the end of the relevant period (excluding any amount calculated in accordance with paragraph (b));
(b) where the contract provides for payment for materials, an amount equal to the value of any materials manufactured on site or brought onto site for the purposes of the works during the period

from the commencement of the contract to the end of the relevant period; and

(c)   any other amount or sum which the contract specifies shall be payable during or in respect of the period from the commencement of the contract to the end of the relevant period.

(3) The aggregate of any sums which have been paid or are due for payment by way of instalments, stage or periodic payments during the period from the commencement of the contract to the end of the relevant period.

(4) An amount calculated in accordance with this paragraph shall not exceed the difference between-

(a)   the contract price; and

(b)   the aggregate of the instalments or stage or periodic payments which have become due.

Dates for payment

3. Where the parties to a construction contract fail to provide an adequate mechanism for determining either what payments become due under the contract, or when they become due for payment, or both, the relevant provisions of paragraphs 4 to 7 shall apply.

4. Any payment of a kind mentioned in paragraph 2 shall become due on whichever of the following dates occurs later—

(a)   the expiry of 7 days following the relevant period mentioned in paragraph 2(1); or

(b)   the making of a claim by the payee.

5. The final payment payable under a relevant construction contract, namely the payment of an amount equal to the difference (if any) between—

(a)   the contract price; and

(b)   the aggregate of any instalment or stage or periodic payments which have become due under the contract,

shall become due on the expiry of—

(a)   30 days following completion of the work; or

(b)   the making of a claim by the payee,

whichever is the later.

6. Payment of the contract price under a construction contract (not being a relevant construction contract) shall become due on—

(a)   the expiry of 30 days following the completion of the work; or

(b)   the making of a claim by the payee,

whichever is the later

7. Any other payment under a construction contract shall become due—

(a)   on the expiry of 7 days following the completion of the work to which the payment relates; or

(b)   the making of a claim by the payee,

whichever is the later.

Final date for payment

8. -

(1) Where the parties to a construction contract fail to provide a final date for payment in relation to any sum which becomes due under a construction contract, this paragraph shall apply.

(2) The final date for the making of any payment of a kind mentioned in paragraphs 2, 5, 6 or 7, shall be 17 days from the date that payment becomes due.

Notice specifying amount of payment

9. A party to a construction contract shall, not later than 5 days after the date on which any payment—

(a)   becomes due from him; or

(b)   would have become due, if—

    (i)   the other party had carried out his obligations under the contract; and

    (ii)   no set-off or abatement was permitted by reference to any sum claimed to be due under one or more other contracts, give notice to the other party to the contract specifying the amount (if any) of the payment he has made or proposes to make, specifying to what the payment relates and the basis on which that amount is calculated.

Notice of intention to withhold payment

10. Any notice of intention to withhold payment mentioned in Article 10 of the 1997 Order shall be given not later than 7 days before the final date for payment determined either in accordance with the construction contract, or where no such provision is made in the contract, in accordance with paragraph 8.

Prohibition of conditional payment provisions

11. Where a provision making payment under a construction contract conditional on the payer receiving payment from a third person is ineffective (within the meaning of Article 12 of the 1997 Order), and the parties have not agreed other terms for payment, the relevant provisions of—
(a) paragraphs 2, 4, 5, 7, 8, 9 and 10 shall apply in the case of a relevant construction contract; and
(b) paragraphs 6, 7, 8, 9 and 10 shall apply in the case of any other construction contract.

Interpretation

12. In this Part-

"claim by the payee" means a written notice given by the party carrying out work under a construction contract to the other party specifying the amount of any payment or payments which he considers to be due and the basis on which it is, or they are calculated;

"contract price" means the entire sum payable under the construction contract in respect of the work;

"relevant construction contract" means any construction contract other than one—
(a) which specifies that the duration of the work is to be less than 45 days, or
(b) in respect of which the parties agree that the duration of the work is estimated to be less than 45 days;

"relevant period" means a period which is specified in, or is calculated by reference to the construction contract or where no such period is so specified or is so calculable, a period of 28 days;

"value of work" means an amount determined in accordance with the construction contract under which the work is performed or where the contract contains no such provision, the cost of any work performed in accordance with that contract together with an amount equal to any overhead or profit included in the contract price;

"work" means any of the work or services included in Article 3 of the 1997 Order.

Index

Index